THE
GIANT
ALEXANDER

THE GIANT ALEXANDER

Story by FRANK HERRMANN

Pictures by GEORGE HIM

McGRAW-HILL BOOK COMPANY · NEW YORK · SAN FRANCISCO

TO
Camilla, Lucilla and Paul;
and Patricia who can
always take over

First distribution in the United States of America 1965
Text 1964 © Frank Herrmann
Illustrations 1964 © George Him
All Rights Reserved. This book, or parts thereof, may not be
reproduced in any form without permission of the publishers.
Library of Congress Catalog Card Number: 65–16660
Printed in Great Britain

The Giant Alexander lived in a big, black barn in Maldon near the sea in England. He was sixty feet tall, which is as high as one telegraph pole on top of another. He looked rather fierce, though he was really very friendly, and he had a thick reddish-brown beard.

One night there was an awful gale. The next morning the giant was having his breakfast of eight loaves of bread with strawberry jam and two bucketfuls of milk when old Coastguard Pennock came rushing in.

"There's a ship stuck on the sandbank," he yelled. "I saw it through my telescope. You must come and push it off or the waves will smash it to pieces."

The giant wiped his beard with a red tablecloth, which he used as a napkin, and scratched his head. "The trouble is my boots are being repaired and I hate getting my feet wet. You know how easily I catch cold," Alexander said. "But all right, I'll come."

The giant put on his special windproof leather jacket and a big knitted cap. Then he followed old Pennock, who ran pellmell toward the beach so the giant wouldn't have to walk too slowly.

"There's the ship," shouted the coastguard. "It's a Dutch one. Give her a hard shove. Good luck."

The Giant Alexander strode way out into the sea, ignoring the waves that lashed his legs. When he got to the ship, he lifted up the end that was stuck on the sandbank and gave it a great push.

The captain and some of the sailors were standing on the deck. They waved and shouted with joy.

The water in the sea was so cold that the giant gave an enormous sneeze—"T S C H O O – OO – OO"—and blew them all down. But they didn't mind in the least, because their ship was moving again and they could sail it back to Holland.

The captain, who was called Hendrik Leuwenhaagen, took his megaphone and shouted to the giant, "Thank you so very much. We come and visit you. Bring you lovely present."

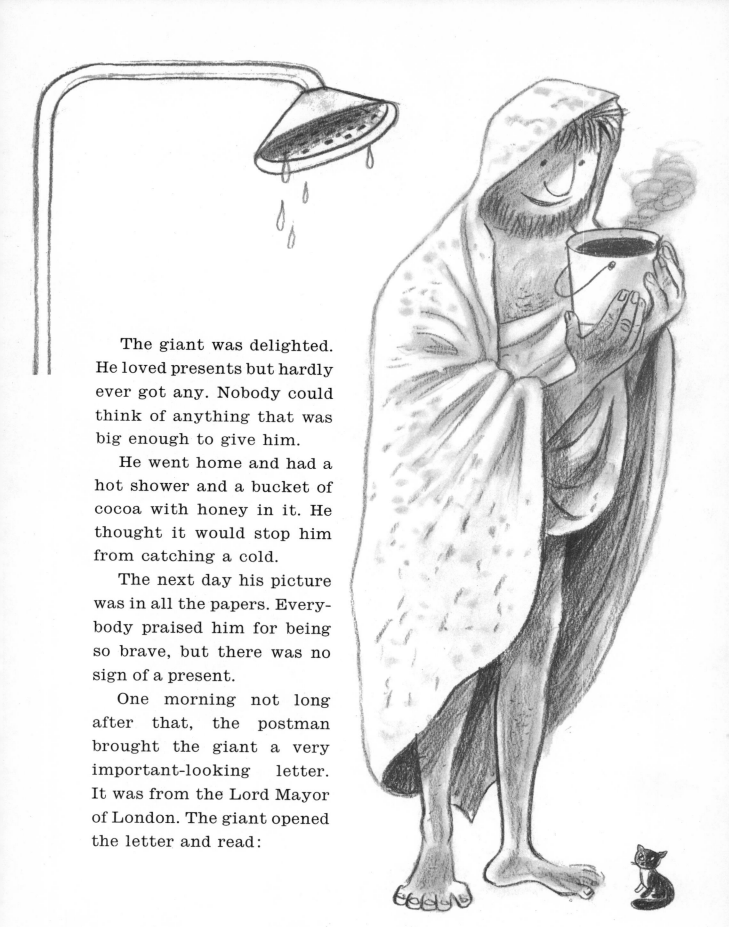

The giant was delighted. He loved presents but hardly ever got any. Nobody could think of anything that was big enough to give him.

He went home and had a hot shower and a bucket of cocoa with honey in it. He thought it would stop him from catching a cold.

The next day his picture was in all the papers. Everybody praised him for being so brave, but there was no sign of a present.

One morning not long after that, the postman brought the giant a very important-looking letter. It was from the Lord Mayor of London. The giant opened the letter and read:

The Giant Alexander,
MALDON, Essex.

Dear Giant Alexander:

I saw your picture in the *Daily Telegraph* and I wonder whether you can help me. I'm in great trouble.

The pigeons have made an awful mess of Nelson's Column in Trafalgar Square. I can't find anyone to clean it. The man who usually does it has had to go to Paris to clean the Eiffel Tower, which will take ages.

Will you clean Nelson's Column for me? Then join me for tea at the Mansion House afterward?

The giant hadn't been to London for a long time. He asked the postman to wire the Lord Mayor to say he was coming at once, and he set off. But Alexander knew the way only as far as the Hackney Marshes on the outskirts of London. The Lord Mayor had to send a special jeep with a big blue flag to guide him to Trafalgar Square.

Everybody in London thought that giants existed only in stories. As soon as they heard that the Giant Alexander was cleaning Nelson's Column, thousands of people came to watch him. There were so many that all the cars had to stop. But not one driver blew his horn—neither a cab driver nor a bus driver. They were all much too interested in watching Alexander scrubbing away at the Column with an old toothbrush he had saved for odd jobs. He had a huge bucket also. He filled it with water from the fountain and put in a whole sack of extra-bubbly soap powder.

The Lord Mayor had provided a special giant's stepladder. But Alexander couldn't move it around as he would have liked. The people kept getting under foot.

''OUT OF THE WAY, PLEASE,'' he roared politely.

The pigeons were so frightened they flew off the National Gallery and didn't come back for weeks. The people miles away thought Alexander was a loudspeaker. His voice was so clear.

The Lord Mayor's butler ran and summoned ninety-nine policemen, twelve of them on horses. They moved the crowds away from the base of Nelson's Column so that the giant could do his job properly. Still all the grown-ups and children stayed as close as they could and the giant splashed so hard that many people had to put up their umbrellas to keep dry.

When he got the column clean and shining, the giant polished Admiral Nelson himself with an old light-blue double blanket. It had been given to the Lady Mayoress just after she had married the Lord Mayor.

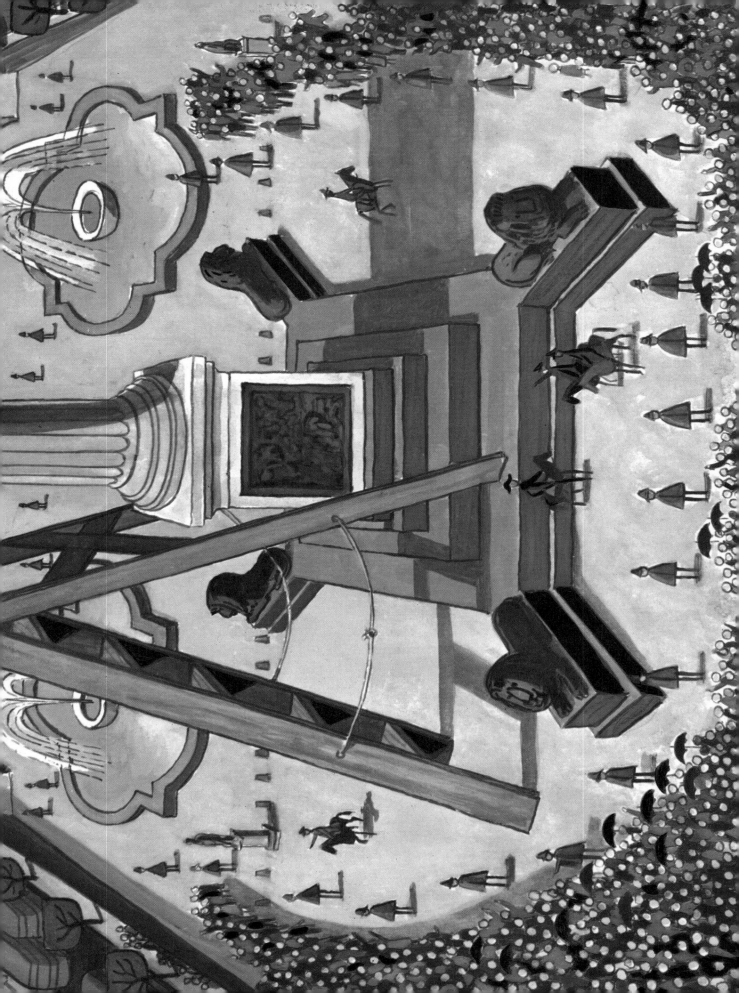

At last the giant stepped down from the ladder. He finished the job by giving the four lions at the base of the monument a good rubdown.

The people in Trafalgar Square were so pleased to see Nelson so clean that they began to clap and sing, "For he's a jolly good fellow." The policemen sang loudest of all.

Then the giant walked over to the Mansion House. The Lord Mayor opened the front door himself, and invited him into the dining room. It was a lovely big room, but the giant kept bumping his head against the chandeliers.

Tea was served by the butler and three footmen. Alexander drank his out of a big golden soup tureen.

"It was very good of you to come here," said the Lord Mayor. "Perhaps you could manage it two or three times a year. London's such a dirty place."

He gave the giant an enormous envelope with a large check inside. The giant was delighted because he needed a lot of money to buy enough food for himself.

Although he was rather tired after his busy day, he walked back to Maldon in a little over an hour. It was over 40 miles, but now he knew the way.

Two days later the giant had his weekly bath in the local swimming pool. Nobody could swim while he was there.

He had just returned home when a very excited little man knocked at his door. The giant lifted him onto his kitchen table so that they could talk more easily.

"My name," said the little man, "is Robin Bingo. I'm a farmer and not a very good one, I'm afraid. Yesterday I was plowing a field of mine called the Six-Acre Sally. I hit an enormous lump. I picked it up and it glinted and sparkled. So I took it to the Public Library. The lady there said it was an old silver dish and very valuable. I've looked and there are many more things like it in the

field. The trouble is, I haven't got enough money to pay people to dig them out, and so—I came to ask if you could help."

The giant smiled. He loved hard work and lots of exercise, particularly digging. "Of course I will," he said. "But we will need a special pick and shovel."

Poor Robin Bingo. He was so tired after all the excitement. The giant very kindly lifted him up again and very carefully slipped him inside his coat pocket. After that, they went over to the blacksmith's shop and ordered a pick and shovel in a super giant size. Then they went to the Six-Acre Sally.

"We must go home and plan this very carefully," said the giant. "How I wish I had some really big boots! Your field *is* muddy."

The giant with Robin Bingo in his pocket walked back to his place. A large van was drawn up outside the ramshackle old barn and six sailors were taking two large, long boxes out of it. The giant was most surprised to see Captain Leuwenhaagen.

"We bring your present at last," he said. "It takes very long time, much leather to make such big boots. We hope they fit."

The Giant Alexander was very pleased. Here was a *real* present for him, and a useful one too.

He sat down on top of the van, took off his shoes and tried on the

long boots. They were beautifully made and fitted perfectly—just the thing for Farmer Bingo's muddy field.

The Dutchmen had also brought him some cider—six barrels of it—and an enormous Dutch cheese. To celebrate, the sailors fetched some glasses and filled them, but the giant drank his cider out of the barrel.

Captain Leuwenhaagen then made a speech about how brave the giant had been. It was so long that the giant dozed quietly for three-quarters of an hour.

At long last the sailors drove off in the van.

It was only when the giant was going to bed that he remembered that poor Robin Bingo was still inside his pocket. But Robin was fast asleep. The giant took him out and put him down gently before he woke him up. Robin and the giant decided to meet again as soon as the blacksmith had made the pick and shovel.

Even with the special giant-size pick and shovel, it took the giant three weeks to dig all the ancient silver treasure out of the Six-Acre Sally. There were dishes and plates, cups and beakers, bracelets and rings, and lots of coins. The giant had to use a magnifying glass because some of the things were so small, but he was very, very careful to see that nothing was thrown away. He put all the soil he dug through a huge sievelike thing, called a riddle, before a truck took it away.

Farmer Bingo set up long trestle tables in all his barns and cow sheds and placed the silver treasure on them.

When it was ready, an expert came from the British Museum and examined each piece over and over. He said everything was very old and tremendously precious. He also said that Farmer Bingo and the giant couldn't keep the things, because they were treasure trove really and belonged to the Queen. But he told them that they'd get lots of money for them.

And the expert was right. They did get lots of money, so Robin Bingo was poor no longer. Half of all the money he gave to Alexander. Everyone thought this was very fair.

The giant worked so hard to fill all the holes and make the field smooth and level again that, after all his digging and all his filling and smoothing, he slept for three whole days and nights. He snored so loudly that the noise broke all his neighbors' windows. On the first night the sound even started the church bells ringing. Nobody minded very much about the windows because the weather was warm, but the snoring was rather hard to bear.

The neighbors got so used to the noise, however, that when at last it stopped on a Saturday morning everyone worried about the silence. As there was no school, the mothers told their children, "Run along and see if the giant is all right. He's so quiet that we're afraid he may be ill."

A few children peeped inside the barn just as the giant was waking up. When he walked out of the front door to stretch, he saw hundreds more running toward him from all directions.

When the boys and girls got near enough, they all shouted at once, "ARE YOU ALL RIGHT, GIANT ALEXANDER?"

The giant was so pleased that he couldn't say anything for a minute. He knew many of the children had always been frightened of him because he was so big. Now he suddenly realized that they weren't afraid any more.

He bent down as low as he could and said very politely, "Yes, thank you, I'm very well indeed." Then he said, "Would you all like to come and have breakfast with me? I'm going to have roast pork sausages, fried onions and fried potatoes."

As he said this, the children's eyes grew bigger and bigger and rounder and rounder. They had never had sausages *and* onions *and*

potatoes for breakfast. "Oh yes, please!" they yelled, and rushed home to tell their mothers.

The giant sent Robin Bingo to get a truckload of sausages. Then he went to Robin's barn and stuffed his pockets with onions. After that he took some sacks of potatoes and started cooking.

In no time at all the boys and girls were back, shouting and laughing. They sat all over his lawn and his paths. They climbed his trees and hedges. There were so many, they perched on his gates and walls.

The Giant Alexander gave each boy and girl an enormous and wonderful breakfast.

Don't ask how he got that many knives and forks. Even giants have their secrets. But we do know to this very day, any Maldon child can tell you that "A Giant's Treat" means roast pork sausages, fried onions and fried potatoes for breakfast.

EXPLORING CANADA FROM SEA TO SEA

Published by
THE NATIONAL GEOGRAPHIC SOCIETY
MELVIN M. PAYNE, *President*
MELVILLE BELL GROSVENOR, *Editor-in-Chief*
GILBERT M. GROSVENOR, *Editor*

Prepared by
THE SPECIAL PUBLICATIONS DIVISION
ROBERT L. BREEDEN, *Editor*
DONALD J. CRUMP, *Associate Editor*
PHILIP B. SILCOTT, *Manuscript Editor*
EDWARDS PARK, BERRY REECE, *Project Editors*
JOHANNA G. FARREN, CYNTHIA R. RAMSAY,
 LINDA BRIDGE, PEGGY WINSTON, *Research*
MARY ANN HARRELL, *Style*
RONALD M. FISHER, MARY ANN HARRELL,
 EDWARDS PARK, BERRY REECE,
 GERALD S. SNYDER, *Picture Legends*
LUBA BALKO, MARGARET S. DEAN, *Production
 and Editorial Assistants*

Illustrations and Design

MICHAEL E. LONG, *Picture Editor*
JOSEPH A. TANEY, *Art Director*
JOSEPHINE B. BOLT, *Assistant Art Director*

Production and Printing
RONALD M. FISHER, *Production*
JAMES R. WHITNEY, *Engraving and Printing*

Revision Staff
PHILIP B. SILCOTT, *Manuscript Editor;* BRYAN D.
 HODGSON, *Picture Editor;* GERALDINE LINDER,
 Illustrations Research; MARJORIE W. CLINE, LINDA
 BRIDGE, *Research;* RONALD M. FISHER, WILLIAM
 R. GRAY, *Picture Legends;* ROBERT W. MESSER,
 Production; MARGARET M. SKEKEL, *Production
 Assistant;* JOHN R. METCALFE, *Engraving and
 Printing*

*Arms swinging and boots gleaming, sentinels
change the guard near the Peace Tower on Parliament Hill in Ottawa, capital of Canada. Overleaf: Dusk enfolds the Prince of Wales Hotel and
Waterton Park village in Waterton-Glacier International Peace Park, a symbol since 1932 of
goodwill between Canada and the United States.*

NATIONAL GEOGRAPHIC PHOTOGRAPHER JOSEPH J. SCHERSCHEL.
OVERLEAF: JAMES L. STANFIELD, BLACK STAR

4

FOREWORD

THROUGH SIX GENERATIONS a deep affection for Canada has bound my family to that vast country. Three decades before the bright July day in 1867 when four provinces of British North America joined in confederation as the Dominion of Canada, my great-grandfather, Alexander Melville Bell, first saw the coast of Newfoundland.

In this new world, as he wrote in a letter to his Scottish mother in 1838, he had discovered a "barren, mountainous, rocky country, but 'Nature is here in wild magnificence'. . . . I do like it." He returned to the British Isles but did not forget Canada's "bracing climate and pure air." In 1870, with two sons dead of respiratory diseases and the last expected to live only a few months, he moved his family from Edinburgh, Scotland, to Brantford, Ontario.

There that frail young man — Alexander Graham Bell — found not only robust health but also the inspiration that would bring him fame. After his invention of the telephone, my grandfather built a summer home at Baddeck, Nova Scotia, where I helped him fly huge experimental kites and test hydrofoil boats, snorkels, and primitive sonar. It was there that I fell in love with Canada — and there, every summer, I return with my family.

Through the years I have traveled the length and breadth of Canada. I have learned its past from the accounts of explorers and the ledgers of the fur traders. As a boy, I heard the whisper of history when I played among the ruins of the French fortress of Louisbourg on Cape Breton Island.

In my yawl *White Mist,* with the U. S. Yacht Ensign at the peak and Canada's new Maple Leaf flag of unity at the spreader, I have explored the peaceful coves and rocky coasts of the eastern provinces. By steamer I have cruised up the St. Lawrence River, past the fortified Citadel high on its cliff at Quebec, and on to the pulsing metropolis of Montreal. I have made fast friends in all the big cities, home now to so many "New Canadians" from across the globe.

Today, a spectacular highway, the Trans-Canada, stretches the width of the continent. I have watched it stitch together the lakes and rivers of the eastern provinces, the grain fields of Manitoba and Saskatchewan, the cattle empires and sprawling oil fields of Alberta, the passes of the Rockies, and the harbors of British Columbia.

Thus for me it is a particular privilege to dedicate this book to our great northern neighbor, with admiration for all that she has accomplished in little more than a century, and with unbounded faith in her future.

Melville Bell Grosvenor

Tugboat pulls a log boom past a tranquil island in New Brunswick's St. John River. Forests, one of Canada's

CHARLES STEINHACKER

great natural resources, carpet almost half the country.

CONTENTS

MONTREAL

A booming, bilingual city,
timelessly Gallic,
yet French with a difference

BY JULES B. BILLARD
National Geographic Staff

WAVES OF TRAFFIC rolled impatiently past as I slowed my car from 60 miles an hour, trying to get my bearings. An expressway sign glared its warning of an exit toward some suburb with a wholly unfamiliar French name. I rushed on, groping for some hint, in a sparkling sea of lights, that would reveal downtown Montreal.

Then I saw it, a starlike cluster high above the gleaming streets, and I knew that there stood Mount Royal with its 100-foot-tall illuminated cross. I took the next exit and, guided by this beacon, soon reached my hotel despite the turmoil of traffic.

Paul de Chomedey, Sieur de Maisonneuve, who founded Montreal in 1642, carried a wooden cross to the summit of Mount Royal as an act of thanksgiving after floodwaters threatening the tiny new settlement finally ebbed. I smiled at the thought that Ville Marie de Montréal, as Maisonneuve called the village, has grown so vast that a cross commemorating the original now leads bewildered motorists downtown.

Canada's greatest cosmopolis throbs on an island where the Ottawa and the St.

Lights star the horizon and modern skyscrapers blaze near the St. Lawrence River in downtown Montreal—Canada's largest city, third busiest seaport, and a bustling transportation center.

9

N.G.S. PHOTOGRAPHER WINFIELD PARKS (BELOW), AND LINDA BARTLETT

Wood-paneled clock tolls the hours atop the Seminary of St-Sulpice, oldest building in Montreal and home since 1686 to Sulpician priests.

THE AUTHOR: *Of French descent, Jules Billard speaks that language well. He writes of bilingual Montreal with the insight of a veteran journalist. A* NATIONAL GEOGRAPHIC *assistant editor, he also wrote the text for the Society's Atlas.*

Lawrence Rivers meet, in Quebec Province. There sprout bold skyscrapers, high-rise apartments, new homes, modern factories. The city's sweeping freeways include a section of the Trans-Canada Highway, a 5,000-mile ribbon of concrete and asphalt that reaches across the continent. Yet Montreal's two and a half million citizens live with a flair timelessly Gallic: the young in discothèques and smoky boîtes, families in scores of lovely parks, and gastronomes of all ages in hundreds of restaurants—some among the finest in North America. At the city's back door lie the Laurentian Mountains, world-renowned for skiing.

Field Marshal the Viscount Montgomery once called Canada "a hinge between the Old World and the New; a hinge of purest gold." Nowhere, I think, does the hinge glisten in sharper focus than in Montreal.

The morning after my arrival I headed by taxi for Old Montreal beside the St. Lawrence, where the metropolis had its beginnings. My driver voiced the pride of all Montrealers when he told me that his city, one of Canada's chief seaports and transportation centers, would someday be "*the* city of this continent."

It was near the site of the old section that Jacques Cartier landed more than four centuries ago, when he could navigate no farther against the rapids. Close by the hill he found an Indian settlement, and read to the tribesmen from the Gospel of St. John.

In Old Montreal cobblestones uncovered in a restoration project help re-create the city's past. The domed Bonsecours Market, built in 1845 as the City Hall, became a public market in 1879; renovation in 1964 transformed it into a municipal office building. The distant spire draws worshipers to the waterfront's Notre-Dame-de-Bon-Secours—often called the Sailor's Church. At left, a waitress pours an apéritif at Les Filles du Roy, one of many Old Montreal restaurants.

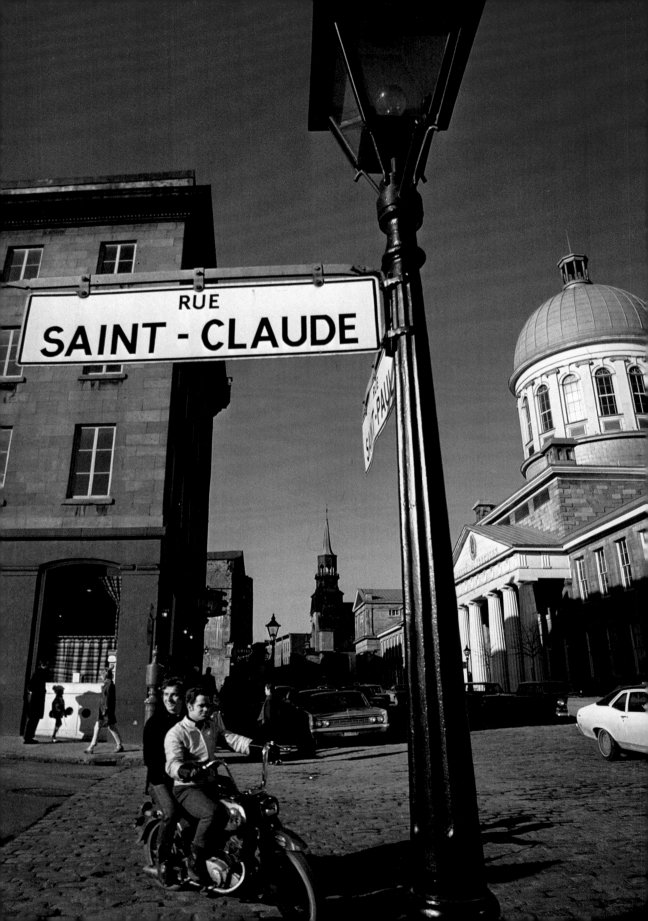

After naming the height Mont Réal (Mount Royal), he sailed back downstream.

In 1611 Samuel de Champlain established a short-lived trading post on the island of Montreal. He named an adjacent island Île Ste. Hélène for his wife, a child bride of 12. In the mid-1960's engineers enlarged Île Ste. Hélène, extended Mackay Pier, and created a new island for the structures of Expo 67, Canada's World's Fair —a salute to the 100th anniversary of the Canadian Confederation and a shining monument to the city's agelessness.

The fever of building and rebuilding that swept Montreal for Expo 67 penetrated even the narrow streets and dilapidated warehouses of Old Montreal. Restoration in this historic area preserves the past while ensuring that the buildings remain livable and useful. Smart boutiques and fashionable restaurants do business behind antique façades. People dwell in elegant apartments within buildings that have known the tread of history.

Here stands Château de Ramezay, built in 1705, once the home of colonial governors. Now a museum, the building served as headquarters for Gen. Benedict Arnold when his troops occupied Montreal after their defeat at Quebec in 1775. Benjamin Franklin stayed at the chateau while trying unsuccessfully to recruit French-Canadian support for the rebellious colonies.

The section's most venerable building is the Seminary of St-Sulpice; it dates from 1683 and still houses Sulpician priests. Notre-Dame-de-Bon-Secours, several blocks away in the market district, is older—it dates from 1657, but was rebuilt in 1771. The ship models hanging from its ceiling remind you that this was a sailor's church.

Preserving the name of Maisonneuve's settlement is Place Ville Marie, first of the huge new building complexes downtown.

Gallic delights tempt a passer-by on Ste-Catherine Street. Two-thirds of Montreal's 2.5 million people claim French descent; only Paris has a larger French-speaking population. Bilingual signs aid English-speaking residents and visitors.

Even on a winter day with snow in the air and temperatures in the 20's you can stroll coatless from the Queen Elizabeth Hotel for a bit of window shopping in La Galerie des Boutiques. This chic promenade, lined with scores of shops and restaurants, knows no seasons. It lies underground, beneath the Place Ville Marie, and is heated in winter and air-conditioned in summer.

A sign in the Galerie intrigued me: "Instant Theatre." I learned that a small repertory company repeats three half-hour performances each noon. I bought a sandwich, slipped inside, and seated myself among other lunchtime playgoers. Eating as silently as possible, I watched an excellent one-act performance—in English. "But of course," smiled the ticket seller when I remarked on this. "Would you have George Bernard Shaw done in French?"

The Royal Bank of Canada building soars 45 floors above Place Ville Marie. On its top floor, 737 feet above sea level, is a restaurant-lounge called, appropriately, Altitude 737. From its windows, diners get a breathtaking view of the dynamic metropolis and the bustling St. Lawrence River.

Higher yet is Place Victoria: 47 stories. Place Bonaventure, a trade and exhibition center, spreads over six acres. Place Radio Canada will be home in the early 1970's to the national broadcasting system. Place des Arts contains two theaters and a concert hall with acoustics so pure that musicians call it "the Cruel Hall."

MONTREAL'S SUBWAY, *Le Métro,* links most of these complexes; the stations in the 16-mile system bear the stamp of different architects. Mosaics in abstract and basket-weave designs decorate the ceramic walls. More than a hundred escalators sweep past vivid murals, and blue-and-white cars speed along the tracks on rubber tires.

With two-thirds of its population of French descent, Montreal ranks after Paris as the world's second largest French-speaking city. Yet Montreal is French with a difference. Most of its citizens also speak English. Signs bear messages in both languages,

"World's largest underground art gallery," Montrealers call Le Métro, *the 16-mile subway system that opened in 1966 after four years of round-the-clock construction. Different architects designed its 26 stations, producing a variety of styles in tile or mosaic walls, pillars, seats, and murals. The Berri-De Montigny station, where the system's three lines cross, displays abstract art—"The Founder of Montreal"—in a lighted glass panel. The stained-glass window of the Champs-de-Mars station (above) frames buildings of Old Montreal. Below, one of the sleek cars runs swiftly and silently on rubber tires.*

sometimes artfully combining the two. In a large department store I saw "*Accessoires de BAR accessories.*"

French and English cultures have long coexisted, but a postwar influx of "New Canadians" has given the city a truly international flavor. A pizzeria's neon sign blinks on and off just down the street from the gold calligraphy of a kosher delicatessen. From a glass tank in a Greek fish market, you can buy a live eel or a whiskered barbot.

Boulevard St-Laurent offered a potpourri of business — the Bucharest Furniture and TV Corporation, Hop Lee's laundry, the Dutch Pastry Shop, the Deutsches Kräuterhaus, and Barbearia Portuguesa, a barbershop. On King Street, near the docks, you may meet stevedores with names like Finnegan, O'Malley, and O'Rourke.

But French-speaking Montrealers see to it that their language flourishes. A customer with perfect command of English will insist that "Anglo-Saxon" shop clerks speak French. I saw bilingual traffic signs with the word "Stop" obliterated, leaving only "*Arrêt.*" In this way some separatists demonstrated their belief that French Canada should set up an independent nation.

Montreal is the hub of the separatists, who during the early 1960's began playing a radical if minor role in the politics of Quebec Province. To unify the World War II effort, the province had relinquished some economic controls to Ottawa. In the postwar era, unemployment and other problems provoked anew the historic Québecois urge for more independence. In 1963, a small band of terrorists bombed a Royal Canadian Mounted Police barracks and several military establishments, placed charges in mailboxes in the wealthy English-speaking suburb of Westmount, and even tried to derail a train bearing John G. Diefenbaker, then Canada's Prime Minister.

I discussed the separatist movement with

Montreal sparkles outside windows of a restaurant on the top floor of the 45-story Royal Bank building, largest office complex in Canada. Below, skyscrapers and a milliner's shop on Sherbrooke Street, the city's Fifth Avenue, mirror the curvature of a wide-angle lens.

Glittering 42-foot chandelier hangs in the stairwell of the shopping plaza beneath Place Victoria. Italian craftsmen used 3,000 pieces of hand-blown glass in creating the masterpiece.

one of its supporters, a former political science student at McGill University. "If Quebec actually broke away from the other provinces, what would become of *them?*" I asked, thinking of the vast geographic wedge that would lie between Ontario and the Maritime Provinces.

"I don't know," he answered thoughtfully. And then, after a pause, "You see, as a separatist, I just don't care."

French Canadians also oppose the American influence in their language. They don't say they are going out for "*le shopping*" as Parisians do, but rather "*pour faire le magasinage.*" A hot dog is "*un chien chaud.*" But sandwich shops take a middle course with signs that read "*Hot Dog, Hamburger, Patates Frites.*"

I had often heard that citizens of France had trouble understanding the speech of French Canadians. The accent doubtless differs from that of Paris, but you can hear classical French in various segments of society. You can also hear *joual*, a patois. The name neatly describes it. *Joual* isn't a word but an approximation of the way some people say "*cheval*"—horse. *Joual,* in short, is the Québecois' version of Brooklynese and Cockney rolled into one.

Though a thousand miles from the Atlantic, Montreal's waterfront is one of the world's busiest. Ships from Scandinavia, South America, and the Orient take on Canadian chemicals, copper, asbestos, iron, and lumber. Grain elevators funnel wheat into the holds of Russian ships out of Odessa and Archangel. From the foreign vessels, cargo slings lower shipments of glassware and textiles, fruit and machinery.

Two other important cogs in Montreal's

NATIONAL GEOGRAPHIC PHOTOGRAPHERS EMORY KRISTOF (BELOW) AND JAMES P. BLAIR

Intermission at Place des Arts: Theatergoers (left, above) chat in the foyer of La Salle Wilfrid Pelletier (right), named for the Canadian conductor. Largest of three auditoriums in the city's cultural center, it gives every patron an unobstructed view of the stage. Critics acclaim the hall's nearly perfect acoustics. Setting for plays, concerts, and operas such as Verdi's Rigoletto *(left), Place des Arts will seat 5,100 persons.*

Wobbly novices take turns venturing down a beginner's slope at Mont Tremblant, a resort in the Laurentian Mountains, 80 miles northwest of Montreal.

NATIONAL GEOGRAPHIC PHOTOGRAPHER JAMES P. BLAIR

Seat-of-the-pants tobogganers hurtle at break-neck speed down a dizzying ice chute at Ste. Agathe des Monts, a resort about an hour's drive northwest of Montreal. In Mount Royal Park (above), a 494-acre wooded expanse in mid-city Montreal, skaters glide on spacious Beaver Lake.

economy are the garment and petroleum-products industries. At the city's eastern edge stand refineries and storage tanks. In nearby communities chemical plants produce phosphorus, fertilizer, and synthetics.

I drove through the loft district, crowded still with those garment manufacturers who haven't moved to more modern factories outside town. Along the Lachine Canal, I saw the tobacco, textile, and metalworking plants that still cling to its banks. The canal, dug in the 1820's as a water detour around the Lachine Rapids, fell into almost complete disuse with the opening of the St. Lawrence Seaway.

Just across the river from the manufacturing suburb of Lachine lies Caughnawaga, home to 4,000 Mohawk Indians whose men have won fame for their prowess in working the high steel of new bridges and skyscrapers in North America, Europe, and Asia.

A cross of steel marks the reservation entrance. In the mission church, founded by Jesuits in 1667 for Indian converts, a choir has sung the Roman Catholic liturgy in the Mohawk tongue for three centuries.

Montreal itself is full of distinguishing touches. Multifamily row houses built during the 1920's and '30's in such sections as the East End and Verdun have exterior rather than interior staircases. These, made of iron, sweep from the sidewalk to the second floor, patterning the street for block after block. Their design gives each family more indoor space as well as private access to the street. But because of the hazard when ice covers the steps, building codes no longer permit their construction.

Balconies are also traditional here. In summer, if you ask an undershirted Montrealer where he intends to spend his evening, he may well say he's "going to Balconville," just outside the door.

The city's proudest natural feature, maple-cloaked Mount Royal, rises 763 feet from the heart of town, luring skiers and skaters in winter, strollers and picnickers in summer. Near the summit, hobbyists race model sailboats on Beaver Lake—to the unending delight of children.

You can go by car or bus part way to the

top. To cover the rest of the distance, you may walk, board a miniature train, or — for a touch of the past — ride a horse-drawn victoria, called a calèche by Montrealers.

Above the chalet, site of summer concerts, the summit offers a dramatic sweep of skyline: McGill University, where instructors teach only in English; the vast French-language University of Montreal; and St. Joseph's Oratory, whose 99 steps some pilgrims climb on their knees and whose votive chapel holds crutches left by those seeking cures through prayer.

BELOW lies one of North America's great cities of vigor and charm. And when the sun goes down, her life force pulsates in a galaxy of light. On Rue de la Montagne, I ventured into a couple of intriguing discothèques. The Mousse Spacthèque, with far-out decor by muralist Jean-Paul Mousseau, provided a space-age "total environment," including the fragrance of exotic perfumes. The place was very dark, lit only by wavering beams of color. As my eyes accommodated to the dimness, I saw a pair of bare, stark legs protruding upside-down from the top of the bar, as though someone had tried to dive right through it. The victim, however, turned out to be only a department-store mannequin, en déshabillé and neatly sawed in two.

At Le Drug Hot, a cellar discothèque with a pharmacy, post office, and boutiques upstairs, the music pounded loud enough to make the beer glasses dance. The lights rose and fell with the volume of the sound. I remarked to the manager, Lulu, that the lithe young girls seemed to do all the latest dance steps with great élan. "Naturally," he replied, "they are French."

In the afternoons, I learned, the conversation of the bearded students and their ladies oscillated from la philosophie to l'amour and occasionally to le séparatisme. But this was night and the music was too loud for anything but dancing. "If anyone wants to talk politics in the evening," Lulu said, "he has to look somewhere else."

Yet the truest joys in Montreal are still gustatory. Across the street at Café Martin, I sampled classic French cuisine in the cozy ambience of chandeliers and rose-red walls. After a creamy vichyssoise, I had an incomparable coq au vin: three large pieces of chicken garnished with pearl onions, slices of mushrooms, and salt-pork cubes.

While my waiter spooned the wine-rich gravy, I inquired about the preparation of the dish. His response was so enthusiastic that, before he realized it, he nearly filled my plate with gravy. Then he gave me a severe look and said sternly, "Monsieur must not talk to me while I am serving."

For authentic French-Canadian food, I went the next day to Les Filles du Roy in Old Montreal. There I began my meal with Caraquet oysters on the half shell. My waitress, Amelia Bourdon, told me they were named for the town in New Brunswick where she had grown up.

At Amelia's suggestion, I next ordered Assiette Canadienne, the kind of fare a woodsman of old would have expected for his dinner. "You'll get a taste of three favorite dishes of the Canadian countryside," Amelia explained. "Ragoût de pattes du cochon [pigs' knuckles stew], ragoût de boulette [meatballs and brown gravy], and tourtière [meat pie]." For dessert I ordered tarte au sucre, or sugar pie — a mixture of maple sugar, cream, and eggs, baked in a pie shell and topped with thick cream. As Amelia set it before me, she declared, "It's nothing to lose weight with, I tell you."

She was right. And as I downed the last morsel, I recalled the plight of Cartier when he visited this island. The Indians who welcomed him to their palisaded village showered his longboats with gifts of fish and corn bread — "so much of it," he wrote, ". . that it seemed to rain bread."

Even today, I decided, beguiling Montreal believes the way to complete the capture of a man's heart is through his stomach.

Carved wood interior glorifies Notre Dame, successor to Montreal's first parish church. Beginning in 1823, artisans labored 69 years to create this Gothic splendor. Saints stand enshrined in the balustrade of the canopied pulpit at left.

QUEBEC

*Past and present mingle
where lonely French "Cesars"
opened a wilderness*

BY HOWARD LA FAY
National Geographic Staff

DUSK IS THE BEST TIME in Quebec City. With the fall of evening, I would join the summer strollers on Dufferin Terrace, 200 feet above the St. Lawrence River. Head-lights and oil lamps stabbed through adjacent Place d'Armes as automobiles and horse-drawn calèches jockeyed for position in the eternal traffic jam. Neon signs atop tall, modern buildings slashed the twilight with blinking reds, blues, greens.

But the brightness, the noise, and the activity ended abruptly at the railing of Dufferin Terrace. Beneath, in Quebec's Lower Town, houses and churches that measure their age in centuries drowsed beside the majestic river that has flowed inexorably past Quebec's austere bluff since history began.

To me this juxtaposition of past and present epitomizes Quebec Province, largest in Canada. Quebec stretches from the border of New York State almost to the Arctic Circle, and its settlements range from cosmopolitan Montreal to tiny Eskimo villages. An area of 594,860 square miles makes French-speaking Quebec almost

Château Frontenac hotel dominates the bluff at Quebec; grass-grown walls of the Citadel command the St. Lawrence River. Road at extreme right borders the Plains of Abraham.

27

"VIEW OF THE TAKING OF QUEBEC," OIL ON COPPER BY FRANCIS SWAINE, ROYAL ONTARIO MUSEUM, UNIVERSITY OF TORONTO

three times as large as France itself.

The sprawling province finds its most faithful reflection in its capital. Quebec City wears history like a dream — a shadowy dream of old battles, courtly generals, and a long, grim fight for cultural survival. Almost from its founding in 1608, this natural fortress has dominated the St. Lawrence. Its name comes from *kebec*, the Algonquian

THE AUTHOR: *Howard La Fay of the* GEO-GRAPHIC *Foreign Editorial Staff has toured Quebec on summer and ski vacations. Before joining the magazine in 1958, he studied in Paris at the Sorbonne, fought in Korea as a Marine Corps captain, wrote fiction, and covered Capitol Hill as a news correspondent.*

word for "narrows." There, at the old capital of New France, the river contracts sharply, and no ship could sail by without passing beneath the guns of the garrison.

Quebec City has always been the key to the St. Lawrence, and the St. Lawrence the key to Canada. The river links the nation's two most populous provinces, Ontario and Quebec. Thousands of vessels course it each year, bringing goods from abroad and carrying Canadian products to foreign markets. Directly or indirectly, virtually all of *La Belle Province*'s 5.9 million inhabitants depend upon it for a livelihood.

More than four centuries ago the great river brought the first explorers into the

LOUIS JOSEPH, MARQUIS DE MONTCALM; ARTIST UNKNOWN

GEN. JAMES WOLFE BY JOSEPH HIGHMORE

Thunder of cannon breaks the morning stillness as British frigates cover assault boats carrying infantry for an attack on Quebec, September 13, 1759. Their armed sloops and supply vessels lie inshore. Gen. James Wolfe (lower right) had landed before dawn with an advance party that scaled the cliffs undetected; he formed his troops in line on the Plains of Abraham, outside the city. The Marquis de Montcalm, commanding the French, attacked at 10 a.m. In a few desperate minutes, volleys of musketry broke up his army. Both generals fell mortally wounded; each died knowing that Britain had won not only a battle but an empire in the north.

Summer crowd gathers for a concert on Quebec City's Dufferin Terrace, a half-mile promenade overlooking the St. Lawrence River. At left, a horse-drawn calèche clipclops through St. Louis Gate, leaving the Old Quarter. Below, a discothèque rocks in Lower Town.

heart of Canada, and after them the first settlers. The enthusiasm of those early arrivals still echoes down the centuries. Jacques Cartier, who claimed all of Canada for France in 1534, found "as fine land as it is possible to see." And Champlain grew lyrical about the "infinite number of beautiful islands having on them very pleasant and delightful meadows and groves in which in spring and summer one sees a great number of birds which come there in their time and season."

The islands retain their timeless beauty. The largest and—thanks to a bridge—the most accessible is the Île d'Orléans, just below Quebec City. There I found farm-steads and villages that preserve the atmosphere of 250 years ago. Fenced farms stretch from the shore in long, narrow strips, affording every family a segment of river front. For centuries, the St. Lawrence served as Quebec's sole highway. The *habitants* even developed steel-keeled canoes to knife through and over the winter ice.

But the ice canoes lay stacked in barns on the lazy July day that I trudged across the Île d'Orléans. The smell of new-mown hay sweetened the air and the bells of the island's six churches tolled for early mass. Save that most of the farmers working the fields had replaced horses with tractors, I might have been back in New France.

In Quebec City itself, no matter how often I frequented the sparkling buildings that line the Chemin St. Louis or the handsome suburbs of Sainte Foy and Sillery, I always returned to the Plains of Abraham. Here the long struggle between the French and English for control of North America had reached its climax.

I strolled past children flying kites and past the simple stone at the spot where "gallant, good, and great Montcalm" received his mortal wound, and another, beyond a rise of ground, where Wolfe fell.

Louis Joseph, Marquis de Montcalm, had victoriously commanded the French regulars in Canada—actually only a few thousand men—for three years when, in the spring of 1759, a British flotilla sailed up the St. Lawrence to Quebec bearing 8,500 troops under Gen. James Wolfe.

Although indecisive as a strategist and bedeviled by wretched health, the 32-year-old Wolfe was a brilliant battlefield commander. He spent the summer debating where and when to launch his major attack. Montcalm waited, knowing that time was his sole ally; only autumn with its freezing temperatures could drive the British back down the river. Then at 4 a.m. on September 13, Wolfe's forces mounted a steep path from the tiny cove of Anse au Foulon onto the plain. Montcalm hurriedly gathered his forces outside the city walls.

The commanders deployed their troops into order of battle. Wolfe's men, clad in scarlet, faced five battalions of white-uniformed French regulars with Canadian militia and Indians on the flanks. The British waited stoically as colors caught the breeze, drums rolled their valiant cadence, and trumpets blared of glory. Finally, at ten o'clock on that pleasant morning, Montcalm gave the order to attack.

The British—formed two deep into the thin red line that would shape destiny from the St. Lawrence to the Ganges—continued to wait. When the French had come within 40 yards, the redcoats fired a murderous volley. The French recoiled. Two more British volleys routed them completely. The battle ended in minutes.

During the annual pre-Lenten Winter Carnival in Quebec City, schoolboys climb onto a dinosaur

Both of the commanders lay fatally wounded. Montcalm, carried hurriedly into the city, died the next day. As one of his last acts, he dictated a letter to the British imploring pity for his sick and wounded.

Wolfe died on the battlefield, hit three times by musket fire. Some said that the young general, haunted by his failing health, had deliberately courted death.

Ironically, Wolfe's victory did not drive the French from Canada. New France's 60,000 settlers have fathered 6.5 million French-speaking Canadians, some 5 million of whom live in Quebec Province.

Maintaining their separate identity while all but engulfed by 220 million English-speaking citizens of Canada and the United

shaped from snow and sprinkled with water for freezing. Polar-bear floats (below) carry the duchesses of the Quebec area, girls from seven "duchies" who compete for the title of Carnival Queen.

JOHN LAUNOIS, BLACK STAR (BELOW), AND N.G.S. PHOTOGRAPHER EMORY KRISTOF

CARTIER

States has proved a vexing problem for the Québecois. I noticed some astonishing linguistic beachheads that English has already established. In Quebec City, I have refreshed myself at a *soda fontaine*, searched for bargains in a *seconde-main* store, and even chalked a cue in a *salle de pool*.

Struggling valiantly against these encroachments, Quebec has intensified the teaching of classical French. In a continuing exchange program, French-Canadian instructors polish their language skills in France, while hundreds of their French counterparts teach in Quebec.

Can Quebec preserve its unique heritage? "Look at it this way," one Québecois told me. "In 1875, 15 percent of the population of Quebec City spoke English as their native language. Now, only 5 percent speak it. Check our telephone direc-

tories and you'll find names like Jacques MacDonald and Aurore O'Brien. Time and assimilation are on our side."

The province derives most of its prosperity from two sources: enormously rich mineral deposits and the endless forests that feed the expanding paper industry. That industry centers on the city of Trois Rivières, 75 miles up the St. Lawrence from Quebec.

Trois Rivières gets its name from a kind of optical illusion. Islands at the mouth of the St. Maurice River give the false impression that three separate streams empty into the St. Lawrence at that point. Champlain erected a log fort there in 1634. Now Trois Rivières is the "Newsprint Capital of the World." Three giant mills turn out 100 tons of paper every hour of every day of the year.

Ice canoes with steel runners double as sleds during a Winter Carnival race across the frozen St. Lawrence River. Sequined with snowflakes, a girl smiles from a sleigh. Tobogganers on the Château Frontenac slide, riding backward for an added thrill, hurtle at 60 miles an hour past ice sculptures created for the two-week carnival.

To feed these mills, and four others on the St. Maurice, 120,000,000 logs annually float down that river. In this biggest and longest logging drive in the world, virtually all the booms begin their journey near the river's source, 325 miles north of Trois Rivières. Accompanied by Larry Jorgensen of the Canadian International Paper Company, I flew north by bush aircraft to follow the progress of a log from forest to mill.

The plane droned up the St. Maurice valley. Past La Tuque, northernmost town on the river, the forest seemed endless. Here and there a maple flamed scarlet — already, in August, touched by frost. Then we were beyond where any maple could survive, and spruce and fir stretched green and somber toward some Arctic infinity. Lakes beyond number and beyond naming pocked the thick nap of trees.

We landed for lunch at a logging camp called Jean-Pierre. "Things have changed since I was a timber cruiser," Larry said. "Then you got pork and beans and biscuits and molasses, and not much of it. Now the company has calculated that a woodcutter needs at least 5,800 calories a day — about twice the normal requirement — to work efficiently, and even sends the cooks to school."

The forest, I learned, no longer rings to the thwack of the woodsman's ax, and the whine of chain saws has diminished. Automation has come to logging in the form of huge tree cutters. I saw one of these machines on a rainy day near Cooper Lake Camp. A single mechanic operated the harvester, as it lurched on caterpillar treads toward a stately 90-year-old spruce. Two great metal clamps locked the lower trunk in a lethal embrace. Suddenly the clamps shot upward; their cutting edges amputated every branch. A quick slice sent the crown of the tree toppling. Another hydraulic shears at the bottom severed the trunk at ground level. The machine pivoted and released its grip; the tree — branched, topped, and felled in less than a minute — smashed to the ground.

But men still fell trees on steep slopes where machines dare not venture. And, because of the perils and loneliness of the work, manpower is scarce. So the paper companies recruit labor wherever they find it. At Wolf Camp I met some 40 lumberjacks who were commuting by jet from Portugal. They arrived in the spring to earn an average of $25 a day until the weather turned too cold for their Iberian blood; then they would jet home for a pleasant winter.

A fine life, they all agreed, except for one disconcerting thing. "When I get home," said Alípio da Costa Simões of Coimbra, "my children cry with fear because I'm a stranger. When I leave again, they cry because they'll miss me. Because of this job, my children are always crying."

Trucks carried felled trees to streams that

"My soul doth magnify the Lord..." Pilgrims sing the Magnificat at the Basilica of Ste. Anne de Beaupré, mother of the Virgin and patroness of the Province of Quebec. Her golden statue shines between the spires. Each of the faithful carries a candle, reading hymns printed in French, English, and Latin on the paper shades.

run into the St. Maurice. Saws sliced them into eight-foot lengths before launching. Seven hydroelectric dams interrupted the river, and the logs tended to jam above them. Gray tugs, fitted with huge bulldozer blades, darted into the jams like swift sheepdogs, herding the logs toward the spillways.

Following the log drive south, Larry and I peeled off for a day's fishing at Lac Rhéaume, northwest of La Tuque. From the shores of that lonely lake rose a palisade of spruce and white birch. As we cast our lines into the cold, dark water, a solitary osprey circled above our boat. Only the splash of a trout broke the silence.

When dusk spread its quiet chill, we headed in with the day's catch, 22 glistening speckled trout. With night the lake became so smooth and black that I could see the constellations reflected as in an onyx

mirror. Far across the water a loon cried his wild heartbreak. Under the stars, in that pure and windless night, I understood how it must have been when the New World was really new.

At Trois Rivières cranes swung the logs into Canadian International's mill and I saw them stripped of their bark, cut into chips, stewed, then mixed with additional wood fibers. Machines compressed the resultant pulp into paper to carry tomorrow's headlines. "The future," Larry told me, "may see the wood cut into chips in the forest and sent down to the mills through pipelines."

Before leaving Trois Rivières, I paid homage to a boyhood hero—Pierre Esprit Radisson, one of the first and perhaps the greatest of the legendary woodsmen and unlicensed fur traders called *coureurs de*

Beyond maple leaves set aflame by autumn, farmers shock bundles of oats in a rolling field on the Gaspé Peninsula. Fishermen at Cloridorme (above) turn lightly salted split cod so both sides will dry evenly in the sun. While most of their "Gaspé cure" goes to Italy, the province as a whole exports 80 percent of its sea harvest of cod, redfish, herring, and flounder to the United States. Below, a cutter near Chicoutimi bucks snow-frosted spruce into lengths of pulpwood.

bois. In 1651, at the age of 15, Radisson left France to settle in Trois Rivières. Soon after, an Iroquois war party captured him as he hunted ducks on the St. Lawrence: "They bourned the soales of my feet and leggs . . . run through my foot a swoord red out of the fire, and plucked severall of my nailes. . . . For the great torments that I souffred, I knew not whether I was dead or alive." But the capricious Iroquois spared his life, and in time he escaped.

The coureurs de bois were men apart. They followed the rivers into the great wilderness, to the forests slashed with silver lakes, to the banks of cool, rushing streams, to the Indians, savage and innocent, to brown-eyed maidens who smiled from shadowed lodges. The coureurs thought like Frenchmen but they lived like savages; sometimes they even donned

Like a ship about to run aground, Percé Rock looms nearly 300 feet high off the Gaspé Peninsula. Frozen waters of the Gulf of St. Lawrence and unbroken miles of snow embrace the serene village of Percé.

NATIONAL GEOGRAPHIC PHOTOGRAPHER JAMES P. BLAIR

feathers and smeared themselves with war paint. The forest was their world and they explored it with exuberance.

In their restless search for China, the coureurs opened the west, and the names they scattered across the heart of the United States linger still: Terre Haute, Boise, Coeur d'Alene. Iron and gunpowder enabled these men to dominate a continent, and Radisson caught the wonder of it in three words: "We weare Cesars."

He and his brother-in-law, Médard Chouart, Sieur des Groseilliers, may have been the first Europeans to reach the Mississippi, in 1660. While his journal is obscure—deliberately so, to conceal the source of his beaver skins—Radisson apparently journeyed down that river and may even have reached the Gulf of Mexico.

Although more than once Radisson's beaver saved the near-bankrupt colony, the government of New France—shortsighted and greedy—rewarded his exploits with huge fines for trading without a license. So Radisson defected to the Eng-

lish and helped to organize the Hudson's Bay Company. Later, he returned to the French fold; and then once again to the English. He died in obscurity, trusted by neither side. Now he lies somewhere in a grave unmarked and unremembered.

The nations that owe him so much have never built a monument to that superb woodsman. But in Trois Rivières, where once he lived, a short street bears his name. Because it was all I could do to pay my respects, I walked the length of Rue Radisson. And I thought of how it must have been for that all too human Caesar, having to "lye downe on the bare ground, & not allwayes that hap, the breech in the watter, the feare in ye buttocks, to have the belly empty, the wearinesse in the bones, and drowsinesse of ye body."

The street ended shabbily at the railroad tracks. I left it and didn't look back. Sleep well, Pierre Esprit.

To investigate another leading Quebec industry, I traveled down the widening St. Lawrence to the Côte Nord, the forbidding strand of rocks and scrub trees that Cartier termed "the land God gave to Cain." Although sparsely settled, the north bank boasts Canada's busiest port—Sept Îles. Named for the islands that shelter its deep, placid bay, Sept Îles—along with neighboring Pointe Noire and Port Cartier—annually ships more than 38 million tons of iron ore to Canadian, American, and European smelters.

I passed a day at the Sept Îles docks watching the big ore ships, riding high and empty, edge alongside one by one. From overhead conveyors, avalanches of iron ore chuted into the holds at the rate of 8,000 tons an hour.

NATIONAL GEOGRAPHIC PHOTOGRAPHER WALTER MEAYERS EDWARDS

Clacking sharp beaks, gannets "fence" at nesting grounds on Bonaventure Island, a seabird sanctuary in the Gulf of St. Lawrence. Adults flap wings spanning six feet as they climb the wind off Bonaventure's cliffs. One of the world's largest gannet rookeries, the island shelters 40,000 of these birds in summer. With winter's approach, they fly as far south as the Gulf of Mexico.

Until 1950, Sept Îles was a sleepy fishing village. In that year, the Iron Ore Company of Canada began building a railroad to exploit rich iron deposits on the distant Quebec-Labrador border. The railroad, and the ore it carries, has transformed Sept Îles into a city of some 19,000.

Across the 70-mile-wide St. Lawrence from the Côte Nord lies the Gaspé Peninsula—11,400 square miles of rocky land jutting into the Gulf of St. Lawrence. In the wake of Cartier, sturdy Breton fishermen settled the peninsula. Through four centuries their descendants have taken cod from the gulf, salmon from the clear rivers, and crops from the marginal soil.

My journey through the Gaspé revealed

Skates laced tight, a Magdalen Islander pedals toward Grand Entry Harbour and an afternoon of ice hockey, Canada's most popular sport. Thousands of youngsters play the game, hoping someday to "face off" for a professional team.

Amherst Island Light on lonely South Cape warns of shoal water off the Magdalens, where ice closes harbors and inlets from January to April. The chain of islands, lying almost in the middle of the Gulf of St. Lawrence, belongs to the Province of Quebec. Reefs and sandbars, a menace to shipping, enclose lagoons where sheep dogs play husky in winter, tugging young drivers on homemade sleds.

a dramatic blend of river and sea and mountains. I followed the long coastline highway—a road through a simple world of fishing villages where gutted cod dries on racks in the sun.

But even in the isolated, rockbound Gaspé, the old ways are passing. The individual fisherman in his dory still ekes out a living, but barely. More and more, the Gaspé's commercial catch comes from trawlers that ply the Grand Bank, east of the island of Newfoundland.

"In the last century," Francis M. Gibaut, a Gaspésien and former official of Quebec's Bureau of Commercial Fisheries, told me, "every village had its own fishing fleet. Two hundred boats used to put out from Percé alone. But now, with everything centralized around a few ports, only a small number of boats put out from Percé."

While most fishermen have indeed abandoned Percé, the town's spectacular natural setting has attracted a flood of tourists, and motels have blossomed the length of the principal thoroughfare.

In the mountains above Percé is one of Canada's finest and most famous restaurants, Le Gargantua. Epicures enjoy fresh fish and game garnished with vegetables from the proprietor's kitchen garden.

Just off the beach of Percé looms a huge boat-shaped rock, like a superdreadnought about to run aground. A mile and a half out lies Bonaventure Island, a bird sanctuary. Gannets by the thousands arrive at Bonaventure in the spring. Each female lays a single egg and hatches it. Throughout the summer the sleek white birds swirl around the island like wind-blown confetti. Then, as cold weather approaches, they fly south, leaving a haunting silence and emptiness in their wake.

At Percé I had reached the end of my journey through Quebec; I seemed to stand at the edge of the world. Gazing east toward Europe, I reflected on the wonders the centuries had wrought in Canada's onetime wilderness. More than 200 years ago, Wolfe had approached his rendezvous with history through these waters. And he had had the vision. "This will," he wrote, "some time hence, be a vast empire, the seat of power and learning. Nature has refused them nothing, and there will grow a people ... that will fill this vast space." Quebec is fulfilling that prophecy.

JOHN LAUNOIS, BLACK STAR

Icebreaker knifes a channel in the St. Lawrence between Quebec and Montreal, thus keeping the river open and preventing shore-to-shore ice jams that could dam the stream and cause serious floods. Block and tackle (opposite) keeps the ore carrier Lawrencecliffe Hall *from slipping into deep water. Her captain beached the vessel on Île d'Orléans in 1965 after she and the British ship* Sunek *collided. Salvors later refloated the ore ship, and she returned to service.*

MARITIMES

Provinces of the sea: quiet coves and villages, a great harbor, shimmering lakes and evergreen highlands

BY ARTHUR P. MILLER, JR.
National Geographic Staff

A RED-AND-WHITE LIGHTHOUSE slipped past the gunwale of the ferry M.V. *Bluenose*, a ship's whistle sounded, and a whiff of cod drifted from a trawler. Seven hours after leaving Bar Harbor, Maine, our ferry eased into a slip, and we drove our station wagon ashore at the tidy Nova Scotia port of Yarmouth. Along Canada's east coast large ferries such as the *Bluenose*, looking like miniature ocean liners, link the Maritime Provinces of Nova Scotia, New Brunswick, and Prince Edward Island.

With my wife Marge in the front seat of the station wagon, and our daughters Susan, 10, Kathryn, 8, Janet, 5, and Nancy, 3, on a foam-rubber mat in the back, I set course for our first destination, Port Royal National Historic Park, about 125 miles north of Yarmouth.

At Port Royal in 1605, two years before the founding of Jamestown, Virginia, rose the first permanent European settlement in North America north of Spanish Florida. Here artisans, farmers, soldiers, and sailors under the Sieur de Monts built a *habitation* to a plan drawn up by the expedition's

Annapolis River loops through the wide Nova Scotia valley that Champlain in 1604 found "most favorable and agreeable" for settlement. Acadians cleared and diked these fertile fields.

Bronze statue of Longfellow's Evangeline stands at Grand Pré National Historic Park. The museum behind the figure echoes the style of the Church of St. Charles, where a British officer "spake from the steps of the altar" to announce the expulsion of the French Acadians from Nova Scotia in 1755. Some of the expatriates eventually returned, but most young Nova Scotians today trace their ancestry to the British Isles.

navigator, Samuel de Champlain. Now restored, the stockaded trading post rests atop an emerald knoll overlooking Annapolis Basin, the bay Champlain called "one of the finest harbors . . . along all these coasts."

Walking through a studded oak doorway at the park, we stepped, in effect, more than three centuries into the past. Our guide, Barry Moody, led us across the stockade's central courtyard, past the original stone well, through the trading room with its cobbled floor where Indians dumped beaver and fox furs. We peered into the kitchen, the chapel, the living quarters. Near a large chimney we investigated an isolation cubicle where Canada's first settlers tried to cure "the fevers."

"Notice that some doors are painted green and the others blue?" Barry asked. "The green doors indicate shops, the blue ones gentlemen's dwellings." I learned to watch doorways of both colors, for the low overheads were built for men averaging a little over five feet in height.

"The place was livable but pretty lonely," Barry continued. "The men faced a long,

THE AUTHOR: *Arthur P. Miller, Jr., and his wife crisscrossed the Maritimes with their four young daughters. A former naval officer and newsman, Mr. Miller has traveled Canada east and west on assignment as Associate Editor of the Society's weekly School Bulletin. He and his family live in Potomac, Maryland.*

cold winter of boredom, the threat of sickness, and unpredictable Indians. So Champlain thought up an antidote: *L'Ordre de Bon Temps* — the Order of the Good Time. He charged each member, in turn, with providing gourmet dinners for the *habitants."*

Each evening the oak table in the dining hall held moose-meat pie, breast of goose, beaver tail, roast duck, broiled caribou steaks, and trout taken through the winter ice with Indian spears. Diners fingered wineglasses, Indians squatted on the pegged floor, and choristers broke into song.

"Whatever our gourmands at home may think," wrote one settler, "we found as good cheer in Port Royal as they. . . ."

We were pleased to learn that the Order of the Good Time still exists. Any visitor who spends three days in Nova Scotia may become a member if he promises "to have a good time, to remember us pleasantly, to speak of us kindly, to come back again."

Bright sunlight splashed rolling green fields as we drove east from the park through the Annapolis valley, the sweet and fertile land that attracted French farmers to Acadia. These Acadians planted the first of the apple trees whose progeny spread a white canopy over the valley each spring.

In his poem *Evangeline*, Longfellow describes how "dikes, that the hands of the farmers had raised with labor incessant,

50

Wharves and warehouses line the busy water-front of Halifax, capital of Nova Scotia. British-built fortress tops Citadel Hill, site of the province's first English settlement in 1749. In Prince Edward Island's Confederation Chamber (right) delegates from Britain's North American colonies planned the Canadian nation. The room, in Province House at Charlottetown, looks as it did a century ago. New Brunswick's Legislative Building (left) at Fredericton dates from 1880.

shut out the turbulent tides;" and the "houses, with frames of oak and of hemlock such as the peasants of Normandy built. . . ." As we turned off the main road toward Grand Pré, we saw traces of the dikes crisscrossing the lowlands.

Standing before a museum built in the style of the old Church of St. Charles, in Grand Pré National Historic Park, we gazed at a bronze statue of Longfellow's heroine. The sadness in that touching figure reflects the saga of the expulsion of the Acadians.

In 1710, the British gained permanent control of Acadia, leaving the peaceful Acadians to themselves. By 1755, however, relations between Britain and France had deteriorated. The governor of Nova Scotia ordered the Acadians to pledge full allegiance to the British Crown. Fearing they might be forced to bear arms against fellow Frenchmen, the Acadians refused. The governor ordered them expelled.

On September 5, 1755, the first of 14,000 Acadians to be uprooted were separated from loved ones and scattered throughout

British colonies to the south. Only among the French in Louisiana were the Acadians able to form a permanent and prosperous settlement. Today, their descendants are called "Cajuns."

Within a decade a few thousand Acadians began to return to Nova Scotia, only to find their fields occupied by Scots, Englishmen, and former New Englanders. They contented themselves with settling on less fruitful acres.

"We're not so much French or English any more," a dock worker in Halifax told me. "We're too busy being Nova Scotians."

To get our best view of Halifax, Nova Scotia's capital and the Maritimes' chief city, we drove up winding streets to the Citadel, planned by the British in the early 19th century as their major bastion in North America. As I squeezed our car through the narrow entrance in a wall 10 to 15 feet thick, I understood why the fort took 30 years to build.

From its ramparts, we gazed down on one of the world's great harbors. Steel cranes fed lumber, fish, and ore to some of the 3,300 ships that call each year. Eastward arched the Angus L. Macdonald Bridge, carrying its endless belt of automobiles. One-fourth of Nova Scotia's people live within 15 miles of downtown Halifax.

Closer at hand, the girls spotted the Public Gardens with its armada of ducks and its ocean liner—a model of the *Queen Elizabeth*. At noon a uniformed commissionaire walked to the ramparts and touched off the daily cannon salute.

Heading south toward Lunenburg, we stopped at Peggy's Cove, where barn-red fishing shacks rim a rocky inlet—waiting for the next artist to paint them. Boats unloaded treasures of slithering fish. From an old-timer sitting on the pier, I heard tales of other treasures.

"In the old days privateers used these coves," he said. "They put in for supplies at places like Murderer's Point near Mahone Bay. And of course there's Oak Island. They've been looking for buried treasure there ever since three boys spotted an old ship's block hanging from an oak tree back in 1795. Dug down 150 feet, but they haven't found a gold piece yet."

Lunenburg's fame rests on fishing rather than freebooting. The town proudly recalls the original *Bluenose*, the best-known fishing schooner ever built. From 1921 to

A mobile's rings and crescents eddy in the art gallery of Charlottetown's Confederation Centre; Canadian landscapes line the mezzanine. A student painter sprays a mural to fix its colors for a children's art exhibit. At the theater in the five-building memorial complex, amateurs of the Circle Players make up for an opening night.

NATIONAL GEOGRAPHIC PHOTOGRAPHER JAMES P. BLAIR (BELOW) AND DAN GURAVICH

Carrier boats take herring from a heart-shaped weir in the Bay of Fundy. Rising tides carry the fish toward shore, and at ebb tide the fence-like "leader" at left diverts them into the trap. There fishermen harvest the catch from a launch. A pump boat moored alongside transfers the fish by hose to a carrier as other boats outside the weir await their turn for loading. Wheeling gulls share the haul by swooping into the nets and swallowing fish whole. A Nova Scotian (left) builds lobster pots for trapping his quarry off Peggy's Cove. John Cabot, brushing Canada's east coast in 1497, found the waters so "full of fish . . . that one takes them . . . with baskets."

1938 she raced the finest Gloucestermen from Massachusetts for the International Fishermen's Trophy. *Bluenose* never lost the championship. In 1938 she took permanent possession of the cup.

I found Captain Angus Walters at home. Builder of *Bluenose* and skipper in her golden days, Walters was "on the beach" at 85. "Those were hard days, pulling in cod off the Grand Bank," he said, his eyes bright in a sea-weathered face, "a rough, risky life. The schooner races added spice."

Was his *Bluenose* still the symbol of Nova Scotia's seafaring men?

"She must be," he shot back. "She's still on the dime, isn't she?"

Bluenose struck a reef off Haiti in 1946, but a replica was built at the same Lunenburg shipyard that produced the original. Though owned by a private company, Oland's, of Halifax, *Bluenose II* belongs to all of Canada. Young and old clamber aboard when she docks at festival time.

From Lunenburg, settled by Germans, we crossed to the region along Northumberland Strait settled by Scots. We arrived in Antigonish in time for the Highland Games. *Ciad Mile Failte* the signs greeted us in Gaelic, "A Hundred Thousand Welcomes."

Bagpipers tried to outskirl each other,

CHARLES STEINHACKER

Hopewell Rocks, sculpted by Bay of Fundy tidal currents, stand near the mouth of New Brunswick's Petitcodiac River. At high tide, the formations show as tiny forested islands. A freighter at Walton, Nova Scotia, rests on a "mattress" of concrete and timber that keeps the ship from breaking her back or rolling over at low tide.

comely lassies kicked slippered feet to the Highland fling and the sword dance, and pipe bands paraded. Athletes from all over the Maritimes competed in track and field, including the Scottish specialty of tossing a yards-long log called the caber.

The Canso Causeway took us from mainland Nova Scotia to Cape Breton Island. Rugged hills that cup azure lakes made clear why Highlanders came to stay during the 1790's. Shimmering Bras d'Or Lakes, an inland sea, divides Cape Breton geographically but multiplies its beauty.

On a headland across the bay from Baddeck, Alexander Graham Bell built a summer home, Beinn Bhreagh. We visited the museum named in his honor and browsed among experimental models, photographs, and notes that reveal the sweeping versatility of the inventor of the telephone. The museum, crowning a gentle hill, reflects in its design the triangular shapes of the tetrahedron, a form Bell used in kites to test principles of flight.

"An extraordinary man, Dr. Bell," said the museum's superintendent, Gertrude Ritchie. "And sometimes mischievous. He once raided the kitchen of his summer home and 'borrowed' four of Mrs. Bell's dishpans

(Continued on page 64)

WESTON KEMP

Wave front of a rising tide from the Bay of Fundy, the white arc of a tidal bore sweeps up the Petitcodiac River. Gulls hover near the crest, watching for worms churned up by the turbulence. Above, a man tramps the gullied waste of mud bared by ebbing water at Minas Basin, a branch of Fundy. Here tides sometimes surge 53 feet—highest in the world.

EDWIN S. GROSVENOR (BELOW); N.G.S. PHOTOGRAPHERS WINFIELD PARKS (ABOVE) AND B. ANTHONY STEWART

Yachts of the Cruising Club of America ride at anchor in placid Baddeck Bay on Cape Breton Island. Tiny Kidston Island lighthouse stands off the trim village of Baddeck. Below, dancers at St. Ann's Bay compete in the Highland fling during the Gaelic Mod, a six-day festival of Celtic culture. Ciad Mile Failte *proclaims "A Hundred Thousand Welcomes." Not far away stands North America's only Gaelic college. Sword dancer (opposite) nimbly steps to the pipes at the Antigonish Highland Games.*

Alexander Graham Bell Museum at Baddeck commemorates the great range of achievement by the inventor of the telephone. Visitors view airplanes and ailerons, snorkels and iron lungs, hydrofoil boats and propellers—all developed by Dr. Bell at Beinn Bhreagh, his home overlooking Bras d'Or Lakes.

to make float wheels for an experiment in water resistance. Another time several Venetian blinds disappeared from the porch. They turned up later in a model propeller."

A paved roller coaster, the island-circling 184-mile Cabot Trail, lured us northeast from Baddeck. The road swept up steep mountain flanks, past wave-washed cliffs falling sheer to the sea, across evergreen highlands sprinkled with flowers, around curves that look down upon each other, and over icy mountain freshets. I braked so the girls could watch a blue heron stabbing the water of a pond. Startled, the bird took flight with slow flaps of its great wings.

For 70 miles we drove within Cape Breton Highlands National Park. Black bear, lynx, red fox, snowshoe rabbit, otter, beaver, muskrat, weasel, and mink roam this preserve. Trout and salmon by the thousand flash in streams near the magnificent Ingonish golf course.

At length the road led us out of the park to sandy coves and picturesque villages such as Chéticamp and Grand Étang, home still to Acadian fishermen.

A drive across the island to the town of Louisbourg, at the Atlantic tip of Cape Breton Island, brought us face to face with the epic failure of New France. With Superintendent John Lunn, I toured the 18th-century fortress called "Gibraltar of the New World," now being excavated and reconstructed as Fortress of Louisbourg National Historic Park.

"Louisbourg was a fortification plus a walled city," John explained. "It was a busy seaport, a snug harbor for a fishing fleet, and occasionally a haven for smugglers."

As we walked among the emerging ruins, he told how King Louis XV ordered Louisbourg built to guard the approaches to the St. Lawrence River. In 1741, after two decades of construction, French engineers

"Arms of gold," the Bras d'Or Lakes thrust deep into the forested highlands of Cape Breton Island. Summer turns this inland sea into a yachtsman's Eden. Motorists on the Trans-Canada Highway cross the Great Bras d'Or channel.

proudly proclaimed His Majesty's stronghold "impregnable." A splendid thing it was, and home to more than 4,000 French settlers at the edge of the frontier. But to the colonists of New England this bastion of Roman Catholic France was a "flaming outpost of the Satanic realm itself."

With Britain and France again at war in Europe, New England mounted an expedition of 4,000 colonists, transported by 19 British ships. In May, 1745, the force laid siege to Louisbourg, and after 46 days the garrison surrendered. The New England volunteers had humbled a major European power. As the American Revolution neared, they kept recalling their glory at Louis-

bourg. They also remembered bitterly that three years after the fall of the fort, England, with a stroke of the pen at Aix-la-Chapelle, returned their prize to France.

In 1758, with the Franco-British contest for the New World at its height, a British force of 108 ships and 14,000 men besieged Louisbourg—and again the fortress fell. It served as a base for Wolfe's attack on Quebec. Then Royal Engineers systematically blasted it into rubble.

Driving aboard a ferry at Caribou, we voyaged to Prince Edward Island. On P.E.I., as we soon learned to call it, farmers tend tidy fields of potatoes and turnips and gather oats and hay to feed dairy cows. The

island, smallest of Canada's provinces, is famous for butter and cheese. It sends seed potatoes all over the world. Many farmers till the red soil part of the year and harvest lobsters and oysters offshore the remainder.

We had heard of P.E.I.'s well-organized camping facilities and resolved to try them. After making reservations, we rented gear and drove to Cavendish Beach, one of three sections of Prince Edward Island National Park. The campgrounds draw half again as many campers and travelers as the 108,000 people who live on the island.

During a three-day visit, we lazed on a white beach backed by red sandstone headlands, tramped evergreen forest, and tucked away meals to match outdoor-size appetites. One morning we took Susan to see the green-and-white house Lucy Maud Montgomery used as the setting for the beloved story *Anne of Green Gables*. The house stands near Cavendish, within the park, furnished as the author described it.

Junior seamen in homemade prams jockey for position, and white-sailed Snipes wait by the pier at Baddeck. Picnickers near Great Bras d'Or Bridge let their fire burn down to coals for broiling fresh-caught salmon. The old lighthouse has stood dark since the bridge opened in 1960, replacing two ferry routes and forming another link in Canada's transcontinental highway system.

Setting ablaze the 64-gun Le Prudent, *British tars crush the last hopes of besieged Louisbourg, bulwark of New France. The following day, July 26, 1758, the great fortress of Cape Breton Island surrendered. A year later, Britain's Gen. James Wolfe made it a base for his victorious campaign against the French at Quebec City.*

DOM NAJOLIA

Reconstructed fortress at Louisbourg (left) overshadows the old town, part of which will also be rebuilt. The Château St. Louis stretches 370 feet across the King's Bastion. A model (opposite) shows fortress walls French engineers labored 20 years to build; in 1760 British troops blasted them into rubble in seven months.

In P.E.I.'s capital, Charlottetown, delegates from all "British North America" met in 1864 to consider uniting Canada into one dominion. We saw the Confederation Chamber in the Province House, polished and austere, looking as it did a century ago. In 1964, islanders built a modern Confederation Centre housing historic exhibits, lecture halls, an art gallery, a theater, and a library.

Still another ferry took us across North-umberland Strait to New Brunswick, last of the Maritimes. At Moncton on the Petitcodiac River we witnessed a tidal bore, the leading edge of an incoming tide. But this was no ordinary bore. It curled ahead of the Bay of Fundy tide — highest in the world.

Kathryn spotted the bore spreading across the inlet with a soft rush like gentle breakers at the seashore. The sound intensified to a roar as the water glided past. Behind the bore charged the chocolate

"THE CAPTURE OF LOUISBOURG" BY FRANCIS SWAINE, ROYAL ONTARIO MUSEUM, UNIVERSITY OF TORONTO (ABOVE) AND N.G.S. PHOTOGRAPHER DAVID S. BOYER

tide in full flood, drowning the glistening mud flats.

In Minas Basin, an arm of the Bay of Fundy, tides sometimes rise above 50 feet. A sailing skipper explained how converging shorelines and upward sloping bottom give Fundy the shape of a funnel. When the tide enters, the water can only go up.

Leaving Moncton, we followed the verdant valley of the St. John River, the route that exiled Loyalists had taken after landing at the port of Saint John. These Tory refugees from the American Revolution — 25,000 of them — pushed upstream seeking furs, farms, and forests for lumber.

In Woodstock I took tea with Miss Charlotte H. Winslow, who told me of these proud, courageous people. She unrolled a scroll that traced her family back to Edward Winslow, *Mayflower* passenger and thrice governor of the Plymouth Colony.

"His great-grandson, another Edward, lost his position as collector of the port of Plymouth when the revolutionists gained control in 1775," Miss Winslow told me. "He later fled to Halifax. His son, 'Colonel Edward' Winslow, fought beside the British at Lexington and eventually settled in Fredericton. Another Winslow, 'General John,' was the British commander who deported the Acadians."

The St. John valley blossoms with farms near Fredericton, New Brunswick's capital. This unhurried town gratefully remembers William Maxwell Aitken, better known as Lord Beaverbrook, who grew up in New Brunswick. By the age of 30 he had built a fortune as a financier. At 31 he went to England. There he won election to Parliament, bought the London *Daily Express*, then became Minister of Aircraft Production under Winston Churchill.

In later life he spent quiet summers in Fredericton, where he endowed a gallery of modern art and a theater. A law building, a gymnasium, and students' residences at the University of New Brunswick also owe their existence to "the Beaver."

Never far away in New Brunswick is the inland wilderness. Forests of spruce and hemlock cloak four-fifths of the province. Bear, deer, moose, and battalions of porcupines own this bush country. In rivers like the Miramichi and the Nepisiquit swim some of the gamest trout and Atlantic silver salmon ever to test a rod.

It was this wilderness that greeted the New England Loyalists when they arrived to build a new life. And it still lures their kin from below the border who come to bask in the hospitality of the Maritimes.

KATHLEEN REVIS JUDGE

Cabot Trail hugs the shore at Chéticamp, where Acadians still put out to fish for cod, mackerel, and herring. This road curves along bold headlands into Cape Breton Highlands National Park. There six campgrounds like Black Brook (left) provide tent space for summer visitors.

'VINLAND'

Newfoundland, youngest of the provinces, meets new challenges but remembers the old ways.

BY ANDREW H. BROWN
National Geographic Staff

BLUE EYES TWINKLED in the strong square face, a face weathered by salt spray and sea-mirrored sun. The man was a roadworker who had put aside his shovel to boil a pot of tea. But he had the look of a fisherman, and to my question he replied, "Yes, it was the new road that took me from my cod traps."

We stood beside a newly paved section of road that leads onto the Trans-Canada Highway, not far from where that great artery meets Atlantic breakers at the capital, St. John's, on Newfoundland's eastern shore. I had driven out from St. John's to Topsail, a village on Conception Bay. There I had pulled off the blacktop and the road-worker had invited me to share his tea.

"Who can tell?" he reflected. "Maybe the road will make we'ns rich, with trucks and trippers, and all that." But his tone suggested doubt.

When he alluded to the prosperity the Trans-Canada might bring, he seemed to leave something unsaid. Perhaps he felt remote from Newfoundland's splendid new achievements—fine ships to serve on coastal runs, mechanized fishing fleets and

Labrador's Churchill Falls once carried 40,000 cubic feet of water per second; now dikes upstream have reduced the flow. By 1976 a hydroelectric plant here will become one of the continent's greatest sources of power.

73

In quest of quiet pools where Atlantic salmon rest during upstream breeding runs, anglers and their guides hike along boulder-studded Grey River on the south coast of Newfoundland. Many sportsmen believe this fish, called grilse when it first spawns, is unsurpassed in strength, endurance, speed — and flavor. Knee-deep in the Humber River — another Newfoundland stream — a fisherman casts his line; only moments later a hooked salmon (below) explodes from the surface.

modern processing plants, copper mines at Whalesback, 5,000 miles of road, and scores of motels. But for the present, nothing warmed the spirits like the happy ritual of "bilin' the kittle."

In many journeys across the province — the island of Newfoundland and mainland Labrador — I have found the people like that, heads lifting to new challenges, but hearts remembering the old ways. Canada's youngest province responds today to a kind of revolution, a new sense of progress.

For generations after Canada formed its Confederation in 1867, Newfoundland remained closely bound to Great Britain and politically aloof from the Dominion. But in World War II Newfoundland became a strategic base for warplanes, and grew closer to her continental neighbor. In a referendum in 1948, the people by a narrow margin chose confederation with Canada.

Wiry, indefatigable Joseph Roberts Smallwood, relentless advocate of joining Canada, took office on March 31, 1949, as the new province's first premier. His loyal adherents have six times re-elected him.

The capital — a homespun place — is growing and changing. With 87,000 people, it is the largest city in Newfoundland, which counts in all a population of slightly more than half a million.

On a late-winter morning I walked along Water Street in St. John's. A damp cloud sat on the city, but overhead the sun gleamed through the mist. I passed the London, New York, and Paris Shop. It displayed miniskirts, but buttoned-up secretaries and warmly dressed housewives prowling for bargains demonstrated that miniskirt weather had not yet arrived.

At the harborside, a sealing vessel, helicopter on its fantail, strained at the hawsers as the first officer checked the sealing badges of the boarding hunters. Out on the ice floes, baby whitecoats waited unsuspecting.

"The Narrows," entrance to the pouch-shaped harbor of St. John's, cuts between rocky headlands. Signal Hill National Historic Park tops the northern buttress. Here, in 1901, Marconi received the first transatlantic wireless message. Time and again I

Town that iron ore built: At booming Labrador City, smoke mushrooms from furnaces that bake pellets of ore concentrate in a 2,350° F. inferno for shipment to steel mills in Canada, the United States, Britain, Japan, and Europe. Open-air miner Albert Reilley (opposite) works a pit where electric shovels scoop up ore and spill it into huge trucks that can carry 100-ton loads.

have joined other windblown visitors at the Cabot Tower, Signal Hill's memorial to John Cabot, and watched gulls wheel and mew high above the sea, making wild harmony with the boom of surf against the kelp-cushioned cliffs.

The coast of Newfoundland has few peers. Granite bluffs plunge into the sea. On headlands, candy-striped lighthouses lift welcome torches. Blueberry barrens run mossy fingers up spruce-clad slopes.

And a cruise in Newfoundland waters serves up a feast of picturesque names. This

was part of the pleasure of a voyage I took one August around the north coast of the island, past Eddie's Cove West, Barr'd Harbour, Brig Bay, Black Duck Cove.

I rode *Northern Ranger*, one of the stout little Canadian National Railways steamers that shuttle mail, supplies, and travelers around the island and "down the Labrador" during ice-free months.

Villages, "outports" to the fisherman, clung to the coast below the Long Range Mountains. Between the boxlike houses — painted yellow, red, white, and green — cod and herring nets dried in the sun. Stake fences kept cows, sheep, and goats out of turnip and potato patches.

"She's coming in black again," said an old fisherman at the rail as we rounded the northernmost tip of Newfoundland and met a bank of fog rolling south through the Strait of Belle Isle.

As we stood off Cape Bauld, the fog lifted

and we could see in the distance the shore at L'Anse aux Meadows. There an expedition sponsored in part by the National Geographic Society unearthed proof of a Viking settlement in the Americas.

Norwegian explorer Helge Ingstad and his archeologist wife, Anne Stine Ingstad, began digging at the site in 1961. They dis-

THE AUTHOR: *Since Andrew H. Brown joined the* GEOGRAPHIC *staff in 1936, he has traveled with camera and notebook from Antarctica to the Arctic. In Canada, he has visited the weather stations of the Far North, and run the white-water rapids of Labrador by canoe. A Harvard graduate, he lives in a suburb of Washington, D. C., with his wife and his son and daughter.*

covered house foundations, fire hearths, iron slag, a stone anvil, and a small soapstone spinning tool—a spindle whorl. Here an unknown sailor-warrior, perhaps Leif Ericson himself, led ashore a brawny crew of Vikings nearly five centuries before Columbus made his landfall far to the south.

The Norsemen gave the name Vinland to the vast country they discovered on their westward voyaging, possibly using the word in the old Norse sense of "grass" or "grazing lands."

Visitors may travel by road or by small boat to reach L'Anse aux Meadows. There they find that the Newfoundland government has erected sturdy sheds to protect

the simple but thrilling evidence of the Norsemen's courage and seamanship.

Premier "Joey" Smallwood never stops telling Newfoundlanders that their economic future rests substantially in their big Labrador backyard. The magic words: timber, minerals, waterpower.

Labrador is really two worlds—a haunting coast and a vast hinterland plateau, where the ground cover is a green, deep-pile carpet of spruce forests, marbled with muskeg and silvered with lakes.

Moreover, Labrador lives in two ages. Along the coast, Grenfell Mission hospitals and nursing stations have made me welcome. I count friends among the workers there, who care with skilled hands and minds for settlers, Indians, and Eskimos, striving to improve the lot of folk tied to a frugal land. Schools established by the Grenfell Mission are staffed and run by the provincial school system now.

"How do you do it?" I asked Dr. Anthony Paddon at North West River. "How do you attend to patients scattered across an area the size of Massachusetts?"

Weathered sheds and racks for splitting, salting, and drying cod rest on stilts at the east-coast fishing village of Hibbs Hole. Much stouter than they look, the spruce frameworks withstand roaring gales and the crash of surf. On choppy Bonavista Bay, fishermen net the "king cod."

JOHN DE VISSER, BLACK STAR

N.G.S. PHOTOGRAPHER EMORY KRISTOF (ABOVE) AND HARRY S. C. YEN, N.G.S. STAFF

Unearthing a Viking fire hearth on the island of Newfoundland, Norwegian explorer Helge Ingstad finds evidence that Norsemen reached the New World five centuries before Columbus. In eight years of work at L'Anse aux Meadows, scientists aided by grants from the National Geographic Society have unearthed numerous traces of Norse dwellings. Women used the soapstone whorl in spinning a shaft to twist wool into yarn.

"When we had just boats and dog sleds, it was hard," Tony Paddon admitted, "but with airplanes—and the Mission now has its own de Havilland Beaver—it's a good deal faster. Well...that is, if we're not downed by a blizzard, don't run out of gas, or can't land because of slush and weak ice during fall freeze and spring breakup."

Once in a September snowstorm I flew into Wabush airport, on Labrador's iron frontier. Vast open-pit mines here and in

the Carol Lake deposits at Labrador City have boosted the output of Labrador iron ore to 22 million tons annually. At Schefferville, 150 miles north, the Iron Ore Company of Canada scoops up much of this total, all of it shipped out over the Quebec, North Shore, and Labrador Railroad to Sept Îles on the Gulf of St. Lawrence.

In a bush plane I hopped to Twin Falls on the Unknown River, where a hydroelectric plant produces power for the iron mines. The superintendent drove me to nearby Churchill Falls, where the mighty Churchill River plunged 245 feet, then raced over steep rapids. In a 16-mile span, the stream dropped a total of 1,040 feet.

Above the cataract, the British Newfoundland Corp., Ltd., has impounded the waters of the Churchill River drainage system to form a 2,520-square-mile reservoir. Engineers are diverting the flow from this vast new lake around the falls and are starting to channel it through inclined shafts to a powerhouse 1,100 feet underground. There eleven 648,000-horsepower turbines will convert the energy of the plunging water into electricity for use in Newfoundland and Quebec. When completed in 1976, the installation will provide one of North America's greatest power sources, generating 5.2 million kilowatts a year.

On a high terrace at the mouth of the Churchill sprawls the great Goose Bay Air Base, where the U. S. Air Force is a paying guest. I have watched planes lumber into the air from "Goose" (Newfoundland's major airport is Gander) on armed patrol of the northern approaches to our hemisphere.

But the advent of the nuclear age does not yet preclude in Labrador the pleasure of drifting in a canoe under the full moon, hearkening to the huskies ashore as they lift their lonely howls to the star-glitter of the northern night.

OTTAWA TORONTO

*Capital cities: Old World pageantry
on Parliament Hill, commerce and
culture in a bustling center of finance*

BY EDWARDS PARK

WE HAD SPED out of Montreal on the Metropolitan Boulevard, crossed the Ottawa River near its confluence with the St. Lawrence, and rolled westward on the Trans-Canada Highway. Abruptly the feeling of the countryside changed. At first we were puzzled, but my wife Jean soon caught the difference: "No more French."

Of course. Signs which had warned of an "école/school" now bore the single word "school." Filling stations no longer offered "gaz." Quebec's Gallic aura had disappeared. We had entered the Province of Ontario, where the population is a vigorous pasticcio of nationalities, where the economy rockets upward with an ever-increasing amount of thrust, where the atmosphere is simply—well, Canadian.

With sternly English signs, the highway

Canada's Parliament Buildings set aglow an Ottawa evening. Floodlit Peace Tower spires above the Senate and House of Commons. East Block (left) holds offices of the Prime Minister.

MALAK

83

With bagpipes skirling, Her Majesty's Canadian Guards march on Parliament Hill. The ceremony of Changing the Guard in Ottawa began with a visit by Queen Elizabeth II in 1959. Now hundreds of people gather on summer mornings to watch the ritual near the Peace Tower.

led us straight to Ottawa, capital of Canada. There, on Parliament Hill, government buildings form an enclave secluded from commercial clatter. Ottawa's Parliament Buildings, as Gothic as London's, cluster below the 291-foot Peace Tower, a landmark whose carillon resounds for miles. Trees tinged by early autumn washed against the gray walls. The steep-pitched roofs, built to shed snow, recalled castles in Grimms' fairy tales.

At the base of the Peace Tower stood a Royal Canadian Mounted Policeman, his ceremonial tunic a blaze of scarlet. Tourists surrounded this young constable, snapping pictures. A visitor to Ottawa once asked a Mountie how many times a day he was photographed.

"About 150 times an hour in the summer."

"What question are you asked the most?"

"How many times a day do I get my picture taken."

Guided tours through the Parliament Buildings start beneath the Peace Tower. They lead through the Memorial Chamber, where a Book of Remembrance contains the names of the nation's fallen in the two world wars and in Korea. Each day a single page is turned, and usually among the many visitors one or two have scheduled their arrival to see a remembered name.

When Parliament sits, the tours include the visitors' gallery of the Senate and of the House of Commons, where we arrived in time for the question period—an open

THE AUTHOR: *With a New Englander's sense of history, Edwards Park traces the distinctively Canadian story of Ontario. He worked as a journalist in Australia, where he met his wife Jean, was for 14 years a member of the Society's editorial staff, and is presently on the board of editors of* Smithsonian *magazine.*

season on the government in power. Members of Her Majesty's Loyal Opposition fire questions like bullets, many aimed at some embarrassing flaw in their opponents' political armor. And the Prime Minister and his colleagues of Her Majesty's Government sometimes parry with traditional replies: "The honorable Member's query will be taken under advisement, and a full report made after further study."

In the gallery, we found that earphones

had been installed at each seat to provide translations of French to English or vice versa. Ontario may speak English, but official Ottawa, symbol and soul of Canada, remains carefully bilingual.

Elevators hoisted us past the carillon in the Peace Tower. "It all seems so nice and new," a lady stage-whispered to her companion. "Elevators and air conditioning and all."

"The government of Canada is only a century old, madam," the guide reminded her. "And most of the Parliament Buildings burned in 1916. The present buildings were completed in 1922 in the same style."

From the Observation Gallery, we gazed down on the metropolis. Until 1826 only a few settlers lived here on the banks of the Ottawa River. In that year Col. John By of the Royal Engineers arrived from Britain to build a 123-mile-long canal linking the river to Lake Ontario. With such a waterway, vessels from Montreal would not have to pass up the St. Lawrence where the river flowed past the guns of the Americans on the south bank. The War of 1812 remained too raw a memory for Canadians to relish this passage.

By 1832, when the Rideau Canal was completed, a settlement had mushroomed to house the engineers, who named it Bytown after their colonel.

In the mid-19th century, Upper Canada (Ontario) joined with Lower Canada (Quebec), and the big, well-known cities vied to be chosen capital of this federated colony. Bytown, a logging community of 10,000 people, resolved to try for the honor. Since the name lacked glamor, the town fathers changed it to Ottawa—an intriguing Indian word with a swing to it.

In 1857, to everyone's astonishment, Queen Victoria chose Ottawa as the capital. The town lay suitably centered between Upper and Lower Canada and far enough from the American frontier to discourage invasion by the former enemy. "The Yanks wouldn't even be able to *find* it," muttered Ottawa's disappointed rivals.

They find it now, all right. They gather by the hundreds at ten every summer morning to watch a Parliament Hill ritual, Changing the Guard. Scarlet tunics, bearskin hats, and white belts come straight from London. The shrill of orders, stamp of boots, and clatter of rifles reflect the pageantry of Europe. And yet this brilliant display takes place about 50 miles from New York State.

We watched another charmingly exotic sight: the arrival by state carriage of a new ambassador at Government House, or Rideau Hall, home of Canada's Governor-General. The lovely old landau rolled up the drive of the great residence with Mounties riding as postilions.

Elizabeth II, Queen of Canada, opens Parliament in Ottawa. Enthroned below a bust of Queen Victoria in the Senate Chamber, she and Prince Philip face red-robed Supreme Court Justices. The Speaker, wearing a tricorne, opens ceremonies rooted in England. Though wholly independent, Canada remains a kingdom. When the Queen arrives from Great Britain, she is not a guest but "in residence."

Addressing Parliament during a World War II visit to Ottawa, Winston Churchill cited a prediction by Nazi-controlled Vichy French generals that England would soon "have her neck wrung like a chicken." Churchill's sardonic comment: "Some chicken! Some neck!"

Gazing across the Ottawa River, we saw the Quebec town of Hull, with the Gatineau Hills rising beyond. Fall foliage transformed Gatineau Park into mile upon mile of solid, flaming red stretching over the horizon toward the mysteries of the virtually untouched north.

The Rideau Canal, though never needed for its intended purpose, still links Ottawa with Lake Ontario. Only pleasure boats make the trip, winding south through hayfields, orchards, and hardwood lots. In its 123-mile length the canal raises or lowers boats through a total of 47 locks.

After following it for a way by road, we branched eastward to get a glimpse of the St. Lawrence Seaway. Opened in 1959, it allows ocean-going vessels to reach the heart of North America.

At a motel overlooking the river we watched fascinated as great freighters paraded by, bound inland to Toronto, Detroit, Chicago, Milwaukee, Duluth, or seaward to Montreal, Quebec, London—all the world's ports. They slid past our windows in solemn single file, the flags of all nations drooping at their taffrails.

LATER, I pulled into Crysler Farm Battlefield Park near Morrisburg to watch the ships, and found myself beside the Loyalist Memorial, a monument reminding visitors that the St. Lawrence River was not always an undefended border.

"This monument has been erected by a grateful province to commemorate the services of His Majesty's forces in North America 1775-1784 . . ." read the plaque. It named regiments I had been taught to regard as perfidious Tory bands in the struggle for American independence. "Many units composed largely of persons residing in the American provinces . . ." the plaque explained, "fought valiantly in support of the Crown, forfeiting their property and suffering great privation. They and their descendants played a leading role in the rapid development of this Province. For their service and sacrifice all those who suffered for the cause are known as United Empire Loyalists."

Humbled by this crash course in Canadian history, I looked farther about me and discovered that I had stumbled upon the site of a small but bloody engagement in the War of 1812. Entering the Battle Memorial Building, I spoke with a guard dressed in the shako and tunic of the British Army of the early 19th century. He described how, with overwhelming numbers, the enemy (that is, the Americans) swarmed toward the hasty defenses of our brave boys (that is, the Canadians).

"The Americans had started from Sackets Harbor, at the eastern end of Lake Ontario," the guard told me, "and they were moving downriver toward Montreal—about eight thousand of them, with cavalry and big guns. When our lads caught up with them here, the Americans turned their rear guard loose to drive us away. Four thousand men to wipe out 800 of us.

"They attacked, again and again. And we held them and beat them back and sent them flying."

Hooray for our brave boys, I thought. And then I realized I was cheering for the other side.

The battlefield park no longer marks the true site of the fighting. The Seaway project, dredging and broadening the river, flooded the actual ground. It also covered many a fine pioneer home. But to preserve the atmosphere of the old days, when the Loyalist families were carving out their peaceful, productive farms along the St. Lawrence valley, Upper Canada Village has been assembled and is maintained as a living memorial.

Here stand homes, taverns, shops, a church. A sturdy old bateau rides at anchor, brass cannon mounted in the bow. The buildings mirror the life of the pioneers from 1784 to 1867. Cheesemaker and

Symbol of unity, Canada's Maple Leaf flag waves above Parliament, where it first flew in 1965. The old Red Ensign, incorporating the British Union Jack design, rarely appeared in French Canada. But today Canadians everywhere accept the new banner and display it proudly.

blacksmith bend to their tasks; a water-powered sawmill slices broad planks from mighty logs.

In late-afternoon sunlight, I strolled past the simple elegance of the French-Robertson House, past Willard's Hotel and Bakehouse, past the curving drive of Crysler Hall. I poked into the enclosure of the Loyalist Farm to see the mud-chinked log outbuildings. And I glanced at the palisaded blockhouse, hard by the river. The sun dipped toward the horizon, and the shadows lengthened. A scent of baking scones drifted to me. From the schoolmaster's house on the King's Highway a lady in ground-sweeping skirt, draped with a homespun shawl and wearing a white cap, stepped gingerly along the dusty street on her way to Willard's.

The magic worked for me — I was there, transported neatly in time. And then a deep-chested whistle hooted and I turned to see the funnel and masts of a big freighter out on the Seaway, slipping past the blockhouse with a load of Volkswagens.

Next day we followed the Seaway toward Lake Ontario, driving past the Thousand Islands — nearly two thousand, really. Here millionaires of gracious Edwardian days raised palatial "cottages." Gentlemen in blazers rowed skiffs with young ladies sitting astern, trailing hands in the water and trying determinedly to look as though Charles Dana Gibson had drawn them.

Cargo ships pass at close quarters in the St. Lawrence Seaway. The ore carrier Lawrencecliffe Hall, bac▶

Today the cottages are mere cottages. The young men snarl by in fiber-glass runabouts and the girls wear bikinis and skim the peaceful river on water skis.

Kingston marks the start of the river, the end of the Great Lakes. Blockhouses rose here in the War of 1812, guarding the waterway. Rebuilt as Fort Henry in 1832-36, and now restored as a museum, the old stronghold draws thousands of visitors. The Fort Henry Guard, a group of university students, puts on precision drills in the uniforms of the Royal Garrison Artillery and British line regiments of 1867, Canada's Confederation year.

Across a wisp of water from the fort, on Point Frederick, lie the gray buildings of the Royal Military College, founded in 1876. The cadets, smartly disciplined and snappy in red tunics, take identical courses no matter whether they seek commissions in the army, navy, or air force. They study subjects that stretch far beyond military requirements. Many go on for graduate degrees in arts and sciences.

West of Kingston, the MacDonald-Cartier Freeway runs fast and straight, and if you don't branch off it now and then you'll never realize that rich farmlands stretch to the north, and that the glittering expanse of Lake Ontario lies to the south. At Trenton, we crossed the mouth of the Trent River — and the beginning of a twisting trail for pleasure boats that leads through

in service following a collision, squeaks through Eisenhower Lock on her way to Great Lakes ports.

Endless avalanche of water hurtles 186 feet over Canada's Horseshoe Falls, its spray enveloping Maid of the Mist. *Ontario's Queen Victoria Park crowds the brink of Niagara Gorge.*

NATIONAL GEOGRAPHIC PHOTOGRAPHER WALTER M. EDWARDS

His skates etching the ice, Toronto defenseman Kent Douglas trails the puck after helping clear his goal in a hockey game with Montreal at Maple Leaf Gardens. Curlers at an Ottawa bonspiel frantically sweep the icy path of a 40-pound stone sliding toward its tee.

canals, streams, and lake systems all the way to Lake Huron's Georgian Bay, 89 miles away. Someday I'd like to cruise this Trent-Severn Waterway, to slide through the old Loyalist country with its stone mills, its fields glistening in morning dew.

You still see a lot of hardwood here — oaks and maples — as well as the usual evergreens. But on a crisp September evening, when the last pale twilight shows up distant hills sharp and black, the magic of the north country steals around you.

Driving westward along the shore of Lake Ontario, we began to feel the approaching presence of Toronto. Canada's second city, Ontario's capital, a mighty financial center and inland port, Toronto is booming upward and outward. Industries cling to it like iron filings to a magnet. And these, in turn, attract people from all over the world.

The freeway offered two routes into Toronto: along its waterfront or across its northern outskirts. We chose the latter, since our hotel lay in that direction. Raw new high-rise apartments stood where city

and suburb met. Streets smooth with new macadam turned rough and unsurfaced among half-finished homes.

"At least you have room to spread," I said to a Torontonian friend when we had settled into the hotel. "You have all the way to Hudson Bay."

"It's true we have more room than you do in your eastern 'Megalopolis,'" he answered, "but we are slashing into some of the country's best farmland. Out where those new suburbs are going up we used to raise your morning's Canadian bacon."

Setting out to explore, we drove south, leaving the area of sprawl behind and heading for the city's heart. Yonge Street leads past blocks of clamorous little enterprises, garish signs, hurrying people. Traffic increases to the point of absurdity. Buses, trucks, taxis vie for room on the too-narrow street. If a delivery van double-parks for a moment, if a driver decides to turn left from a right lane, if cars crowd an intersection and cannot clear it when the light changes—instant chaos.

No doubt about right-of-way at the

95

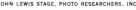
JOHN LEWIS STAGE. PHOTO RESEARCHERS. INC.

Matinee crowd arrives for a Shakespearean play at the 2,258-seat Festival Theatre at Stratford. In Henry V, the Duke of Exeter and the Earl of Westmoreland (right) stand wearily beneath the besieged walls of Harfleur, France, as their king exhorts, "Once more unto the breach, dear friends...." Dancing shoes in hand, Beverly Barkley of the Royal Winnipeg Ballet waits in the theater's wings.

crosswalk. Suddenly a pedestrian thrusts his arm out like a semaphore, steps off the curb, and strides straight into the traffic. Brakes shriek. Engines stall. More chaos. As we inched along it seemed that every car in Toronto must have become welded into a hot, throbbing, fuming mass, utterly immobile while stoplights beamed futilely, red, amber, green, overhead.

"Why didn't you park and take the subway?" we were later chided. "That's what it's for." And, in truth, Canada's first subway flicks you quickly from one pastel-tiled station to the next—an effortless system.

From Bloor Street, Toronto's main specialty shopping thoroughfare, south to the waterfront area, tall buildings with elegant names take over. Here stand the Royal York Hotel with 1,600 rooms; two great department stores, Eaton's and Simpson's; restaurants; museums; office buildings. We saw the Stock Exchange, second only to New York's in volume of trade, the provincial Parliament Buildings, and the ultra-modern City Hall, with its two curved towers reaching skyward like supplicating hands. Finnish architect Viljo Revell conceived this bold design—fitting for a city where it seems that every language under the sun is spoken and every idea voiced.

Colin McDonald, of the Ontario Department of Tourism, once pointed out

that after World War II European immigrants crowded into Toronto because of ready jobs, houses, and schools. Most have been assimilated, but Little Italy remains colorfully cohesive. There, older women wear black dresses, and on Sundays strollers parade as they do in Italian towns.

Driving nearby, we spied a wedding party gathered on the sidewalk outside the Fricassis Confectionary and Smoke Shop. "The reception's probably over the shop," our guide told us. "The Italians like to start at noon and get really rocking by sundown. The Poles begin on Fridays so they have the whole weekend to celebrate."

Along Markham Street little art galleries and craft and curio shops offer their wares while bearded young men and girls with carefully ironed hair sip coffee at sidewalk cafes. Torontonians love art. A laborer passing a gallery will halt, turn back, and stare at a painting for five minutes.

"Toronto used to be known for the largest hotel, the tallest skyscraper, and the dullest Sunday in Canada," a writer friend told me. "Now we've got some other things: film and TV production, and better nightclubs, in general, than Montreal's, with more first-rate acts than New York's. We get pre-Broadway openings. Even our Sundays aren't so bad any more."

He told me about a friend of his, Harold Town, whose abstractions once were about as popular as packaged termites. "He used to paint in a basement, wearing a football helmet. That way, when he straightened up, he wouldn't crack his head on all those unsalable paintings he'd hung along the heating pipes. Now dealers buy his stuff before he's finished it."

Torontonians also love the performing arts. Theaters and concert halls are jammed, and the slick, modern O'Keefe Centre presents everything from songstress Pearl Bailey to *The Marriage of Figaro*.

Like all visitors to Toronto, we became caught up in sports. On a previous trip, I had been given the great honor of a ticket to a hockey game at the Maple Leaf Gardens. I hadn't realized my good fortune until my benefactor enlightened me.

New leisure center on Toronto's waterfront, Ontario Place (opposite), entertains city-dwellers and tourists. Cinesphere, a geodesic dome, shows travel and historical films on a curved 80-foot screen. Diamond-shaped modules beyond the dome house exhibits and restaurants. From the modules, a ramp leads to the canopied Forum, an 8,000-seat concert hall where visitors (above) listen to a Royal Canadian Mounted Police band conducted by a red-tunicked Mountie (below).

DOM NAJOLIA (OPPOSITE) AND MICHAEL E. LONG, NATIONAL GEOGRAPHIC STAFF

"The Gardens has been sold out completely ever since 1946," he declared, waving the precious tickets before me. "Why, people even pass along seats at the Gardens in their wills, together with their gilt-edged securities. Enjoy yourself!"

I did. The Maple Leafs were playing their old rivals, the Montreal Canadiens, and the fists flew as readily as the puck.

This time we were too early for hockey, but we wangled an autumn sail with friends. We breakfasted at the historic Royal Canadian Yacht Club, still a stronghold of Toronto's old society—the scions of the United Empire Loyalists. Their club, with its bowling green, stands on Toronto Island. We headed for the channel in our host's Alberg 30, a fiber-glass sloop that has won many American hearts. It was built at the Whitby Boat Works, only a few miles east of Toronto—a simple cinder-block building where the hulls come off mirror-smooth molds.

As we nosed into the lake, the wind freshened, our lee rail went down, and a wave smacked aboard. The taste of the spray surprised me—on such a wide inland sea I had almost expected salt water.

NEXT DAY we forsook the deck for an inland paddock—the Pony Club, officially called the Eglinton Equestrian Club. Here youngsters learn not just to ride but to ride well. I recalled that at the National Horse Show in New York and at the Olympics, Canadian equestrians always present a challenge—"A remarkable thing," said one rider, "when you realize how little time and money we can afford to spend on this business."

A blond girl cantered past on a splendid mount. She had just qualified for the Royal Agricultural Winter Fair, an annual event that takes place at the Canadian National Exhibition Park on the lakefront. The "Ex" with its Ferris wheels and roller-coasters had closed for the year, but an auto show would open soon. Without the blare of calliopes, the midway lay silent.

Near the grounds, we saw restored Old Fort York, a parklike enclosure of green-sward and log buildings that the invading Americans captured in 1813. They didn't behave very well, those Yanks. They burned the little village of York. In retaliation, the British captured Washington and burned the Capitol and the White House. Eventually, charred York grew into lovely Toronto.

West of Toronto, an arm of Ontario thrusts southwest between the Great Lakes. Industrial Windsor, at its farthest point, lies south of its neighbor, Detroit; south, even, of northern California.

A nucleus of Canadian wealth, southern Ontario bristles with manufacturing: Hamilton, the steel city; Sarnia, center for chemicals and oil refineries; London (on the Thames River!) making everything from diesel engines to breakfast foods.

But we explored smaller towns, like Kitchener and Waterloo, where the plain clothing of Mennonites contrasts with Toronto's chic fashions. We just missed the summer Shakespearean Festival at Stratford. The town—on the banks of the Avon—set out to enshrine the Bard's genius. Alec Guinness opened the first festival in 1953. Since then the Stratford Festival Company has won world fame, with such stars as James Mason and Christopher Plummer, as well as many other fine actors.

Fifty miles southeast, at Brantford, stands the Alexander Graham Bell homestead, open to the public. It was at Brantford, in 1874, that the great inventor conceived the idea for the telephone. Two years later, over wires furnished by the Dominion Telegraph Company, he made the first long-distance call. All the way to Paris. Paris, Ontario, that is, eight miles away.

With many miles ahead of us, we crossed the great Welland Canal and made for the Niagara frontier. Behind us, the Trans-Canada Highway beckoned north to the wild lake country of this huge province, and then west to the prairies and beyond. But that was for other times.

Curved towers of Toronto's City Hall rise above dancing fountains in the square. The saucer-domed Council Chamber holds an amphitheater where 300 citizens can share in a public debate.

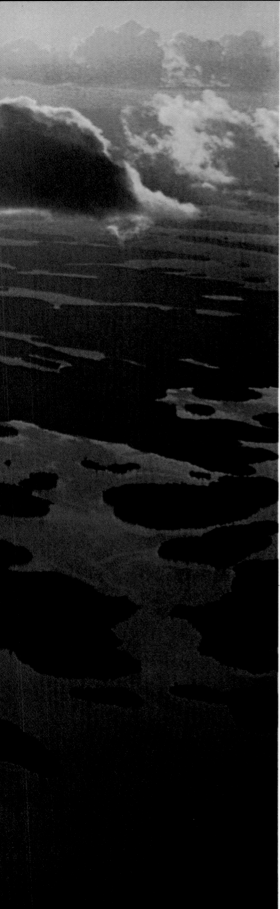

NATIONAL GEOGRAPHIC PHOTOGRAPHER DEAN CONGER

TRAILS WEST

*A river, a lake,
an island, a waterfall
for everyone*

BY RALPH GRAY
National Geographic Staff

ANGLING NORTH from Toronto, we followed roads long and straight across southern Ontario, a region of flat, fertile farmlands. Skirting Lake Simcoe, we headed for the Muskoka Lakes. Suddenly, as if a line had been drawn, we entered a great green ocean of trees that billows west to the prairies and north to tundra. The woods would be home to my family and me most of the summer as we explored them by car, boat, train, and plane.

With the trees began the Canadian Shield —a vast, mineral-rich region that covers half of Canada. Ahead of us stretched a watery world: Glorious lakes, big and small, spangle much of Ontario, as well as Manitoba, northern Saskatchewan and Alberta, and the Northwest Territories.

Picking up the Trans-Canada Highway

Sun-gilded Lake of the Woods teems with northern pike, pickerel, black bass, and lake trout. This 1,695-square-mile expanse of water spreads from Ontario into Manitoba and Minnesota.

THE AUTHOR: *Ralph Gray, long a Society staff member, knows Canada well. His wife, a native of Winnipeg, has often traveled with him and their children—together they followed the track of Alexander Mackenzie, who blazed Canada's canoe trails to the Pacific and the Arctic. Mr. Gray's account of the trip appeared in the NA-TIONAL GEOGRAPHIC. The author also edits a weekly "Junior Geographic," the School Bulletin.*

near Victoria Harbour, we threaded between Georgian Bay and the Muskokas, haven for campers, boaters, and fishermen. Stopping at Port Carling, we watched as a powered lock lowered a pleasure launch from one lake to another. The shadows lengthened, and my thoughts reached back across three decades.

I seemed to see six college boys bringing

104

VIRGINIA POWERS

Paddles stab white water as a decked canoe shoots a narrow passage on the Churchill River. Though the stream surges with rapids and tumbles over many falls, it also holds great stretches of smooth water, and strings together dozens of quiet lakes in its thousand-mile reach from Alberta to Hudson Bay. For the fur traders the river formed part of the watery highway that linked the eastern regions and the Far Northwest.

woods (and the mosquitoes and black flies will bite you, never fear), you must go back. And once you've seen the Muskokas, you must go on, northwest to Wawa, Norway House, The Pas, and Flin Flon.

A neighbor of mine has fished "every wet spot between North Bay and Iron Bridge" in the course of his annual trips to the water lands above Lake Huron. And a friend in Cleveland hires a pilot to set him down on a certain lake every year. In a week the pilot returns to fly him out again —along with a slain moose. The Clevelander always gets his trophy.

"Where is this lake?" I asked him.

"In Ontario," he said. Period.

At the French River, we crossed a thoroughfare that helped make Canada a nation. Never has this highway heard the clop of a horse's hoof or the whine of rubber. This is a water road, part of the canoe passage from Montreal to Winnipeg and beyond. Until the Canadian Pacific Railway pushed to the coast in 1885, this was Canada's only way to the west.

With our son Will, then on a vacation from college, and our daughter Donna, my wife Jean and I gazed into the waters of the French. A fisherman cast his line where fur-laden canoes once passed, the voyageurs straining at the paddles and singing of the good times awaiting them at Grand Portage or Montreal.

Étienne Brûlé established this route, canoeing and portaging from the St. Lawrence to Georgian Bay by way of the Ottawa River, Lake Nipissing, and the French River. Champlain and others extended the watery path to empire, exploring the northern shores of Lake Huron and Lake Superior to Grand Portage.

their canoes through this same passage. The lock was smaller, and the boys cranked it open by hand. Then the carefree crew cleared the gates and quickly paddled out of sight. Those young men were my friends and I. Some thirty years ago we had happily coursed these lakes and rivers for an unforgettable week.

Once you're bitten by Canada's north

Canadian volunteers and British troops battle the Ontario wilderness on the Red River Expedition of 1870. At a steep portage, canoes of the rear guard bring up supplies while other companies haul their boats over rollers made from small poplar trunks — a daily routine for nearly six weeks. The British Government ordered the force to Fort Garry, site

of present-day Winnipeg, expecting a clash with the Métis. These half-Indian trappers, buffalo hunters, and boatmen, who called themselves the "New Nation," had already set up an independent government in the west. But the expedition entered Fort Garry peacefully and established the Province of Manitoba, for the Métis leaders had fled.

We drove on until we reached the stacks of the nickel smelters at Sudbury. There we turned west, and paralleled the paddle tracks of the voyageurs. We had come this way before, in 1953, when we traced the canoe route of explorer and fur trader Alexander Mackenzie, whose expeditions in the late 18th century eventually took him across the continent to the Pacific.

On our earlier trip, there had been no road along the north shore of Superior, and we had crossed by lake liner from Sault Ste. Marie to Fort William. This time we would use the Trans-Canada Highway.

Near the little town of Thessalon, we turned inland and stopped a mile north of the highway. What a difference a mere mile made! We had been promising ourselves a stay at a north-woods lodge and had picked Melwel out of a brimming hat. We found ourselves in a world apart.

"The Algoma woods are full of places like this," said Weldon Moore, our host, as he led us from the main lodge to our rustic cabin overlooking Lake Wakwekobi, known locally as Big Basswood Lake. "The main difference between now and the last time you were up this way is the roads. We have a few now, pushing north into the bush, opening up river valleys and reaching lakes and waterfalls that used to be accessible only to trappers and pilots."

Grain for the world: Concrete elevators at Ontario's Lakehead, Port Arthur-Fort William, receive the harvest from Canada's prairie provinces —and can hold 106 million bushels. Trimmers on the deck of a laker scoop wheat from hatch cover into hold. Their job: to fill corners and level the cargo. The bins annually pour more than 11 million tons of wheat, oats, barley, and rye into ships that carry the grain to 100 countries.

JOHN LEWIS STAGE, PHOTO RESEARCHERS, INC. (ABOVE) AND W. D. VAUGHN

"Don't let them tame it all," I said.

"Don't worry," he replied. "Here we are —barely inside the Sault Ste. Marie gateway from the United States, with all of Canada north of us—yet you can step into the woods and find an orchid or shoot a bear."

One of the guests did indeed bag a bear while we were there. We watched him truss it in plastic, tie it across the trunk of his car, and depart happily for the States.

From our cabin we looked out upon the lake framed by hardwoods. Twice we saw the tiny black spot of a beaver's head leaving a V-shaped wake as he swam to shore.

"That's the animal that caused it all, isn't it!" said my son Will.

He was right. We thought of all the beaver in all the lakes from here to Hudson Bay, from Montreal to the Pacific. They prompted much North American exploration and formed the basis of one of the continent's early industries. No haunt of this gregarious creature lay beyond the reach of the trapper, driven ever deeper into the bush by the fur companies.

Why the beaver? Because the fashion

109

Splashing through sedge grass and shallows on a September morning, trainers exercise a brace of Labrador retrievers at Whitewater Lake near Brandon, Manitoba. In season, hunters come here to bag sharp-tailed grouse, white-tailed deer, ducks, and geese. The Canada goose (right) migrates over nearly all of North America.

centers of Europe decreed that men's hats be made of beaver fur.

Will and I unfolded detailed maps that named myriad lakes in Ontario and Manitoba. Even if you never get to the woods country, it's a real adventure just to study the maps. There are lakes named by Indians (Timagami, Kabinakagami, Winnipegosis), for fish (Trout, Sturgeon, Catfish), for animals (Moose, Caribou, Bear, White Otter), for people (Charles, Lady Evelyn, Irene), for birds (Loon, Eagle, White Partridge), for trees (Birch, Oak, Poplar), for their shape (Long, Cross, Wiggly), and for geographic peculiarities (Rocky Island, Smoothrock, Threenarrows).

"No one has ever seen them all," we were told the following day when we stopped in Wawa, a bustling center for iron mining and processing 150 miles north of Sault Ste. Marie. Wawa takes its name from the Ojibwa Indian word for wild goose. The town has erected a huge steel statue of the Canada goose that can be seen for miles along the Trans-Canada. Today the highway brings hundreds of visitors to Wawa, a base for sportsmen who hunt moose and bear or fish for pike, walleye, and trout.

Not until 1960 was this section of Canada's main street opened. We reveled in it: To our right stretched the illimitable woods; to our left, whether viewed from high cliffs or beach-level picnic grounds, Lake Superior reached to the horizon.

The highway follows the curve of Superior's north shore, then sweeps southwest to the Lakehead, as Canadians call the twin cities of Port Arthur and Fort William. There we got our first inkling that central Canada holds anything but woods and water: Huge concrete grain elevators line the waterfront—filled with the harvest of the plains awaiting transshipment east.

The lakehead for the voyageurs was Grand Portage, which the Treaty of Paris of 1783 determined to be in the new United States. But boundaries meant little in the wilderness, and for many years this stockaded outpost was a gateway to Canada's west and northwest.

On our Mackenzie trek we had visited the historic site at Grand Portage, near the mouth of the Pigeon River at the northeast tip of Minnesota. West of there, Canada's watery lifeline was cut by rapids and one backbreaking portage after another. No path to empire was ever more attenuated than the canoe route along the U. S.-Canada border to Lake of the Woods.

This many-fingered, island-studded expanse of water, shared by Ontario, Manitoba, and Minnesota, drains into Hudson Bay, 816 miles north, through the Winnipeg River, Lake Winnipeg, and the Nelson River. Much of this vast region can be reached only by floatplane or boat. We drove into Manitoba and through Whiteshell Provincial Park to Lac du Bonnet, on the Winnipeg River. There we boarded an eight-place Beechcraft for a fly-in vacation at Norway House, near the northern end of 266-mile-long Lake Winnipeg.

As the plane roared north above the shoreline, the thought occurred to me that

if Lake Winnipeg were in England it would stretch from London to Newcastle, but in a nation of great lakes it is commonplace.

For the fur traders this lake opened up the continent. From here they could go any of a half-dozen ways. They could follow the Cross Lake, Oxford Lake, and Hayes River route to Hudson Bay. They could travel south on the Red River and portage into the Mississippi River system; west on the Assiniboine and portage to the upper Missouri; and west on the mighty Saskatchewan to the Rockies.

Or they could follow a long portage route via the Churchill River to Lake Athabasca. From this lake, shared today by northern Saskatchewan and Alberta, one canoe road led up the Peace River through the Rockies, across more portages, and finally to the Pacific. Another followed the Slave and Mackenzie Rivers to the Arctic. Mackenzie pioneered both these northwest passages.

In the 30 years after the British defeated the French at Quebec, a strange thing hap-

Nail-driving contestants strive for prizes at the annual Flin Flon Trout Festival in Manitoba. Fishermen, canoeists, dancers, moose callers, and pulpwood cutters seek trophies in other events.

In cossack costume, a Manitoban carries the Ukrainian flag at a folk festival in Dauphin. Half a million Canadians claim Ukrainian origins. Garlanded girls smile from a sea of blossoms.

pened to the French fur industry. Shrewd Scots took it over. Not Englishmen, but Scots. They organized the North West Company and, aided by Mackenzie's exploration, stood ready to monopolize the trade.

But another monopoly blocked the way —"The Governor and Company of Adventurers of England Trading into Hudson's Bay." In 1670 King Charles II had granted these gentlemen sole trading rights in all lands drained by rivers flowing into Hudson Bay. This included most of the territory where the Nor'Westers were poaching.

The Hudson's Bay Company fought back

GERALD BRIMACOMBE

with increased competition. Rival posts stood side by side along the trade routes. Bloodshed inevitably followed—a snow-muffled shot ringing out in the wilderness here, an unfortunate Indian trapper relieved of his furs there, and finally a full-scale "massacre" in 1816, when a party of Nor'Westers killed 20 Hudson's Bay men at Seven Oaks, just north of Winnipeg.

Five years later the Hudson's Bay Company absorbed the North West Company, after the upstart organization's financial position became so precarious that no one even attempted to balance the books.

And so it was that Englishmen and Scotsmen, in a land that was to become Canada, fought for a fur empire built by the French and based on the Indians. While I pondered these ironies of history, our pilot swooped to land on the Fort River—main street of Norway House.

The plane splashed down in a woodlands Venice, where every house fronts on water. We taxied within sight of the white-walled,

red-roofed Hudson's Bay Company buildings, stepped from pontoon to open boat, and Mr. John Low ferried us a quarter-mile to his hostelry, Playgreen Inn.

While getting settled, we saw our plane take off for Winnipeg. It would not return until the next scheduled flight two days later. Henry Remple, then manager of the Hudson's Bay Company store, came by to take us for a spin. We hopped into his motorboat and went upstream, waving at Cree Indian children playing in front of their riverside homes.

We turned downstream and roared past the Hudson's Bay post, the Indian Hospital, and into Little Playgreen Lake. In four miles we came to Rossville, a community with a Protestant church, an Indian school, another Hudson's Bay store, and a semblance of a street. Its Cree and *Métis* residents fish commercially and run traplines in winter and early spring.

"I just wanted you to see the entire metropolitan area," Hank said with a grin.

Sidewalk playground for Cree Indian children fronts a Hudson's Bay Company store in Moosonee. Across the dusty main street stands a Roman Catholic church. The town, end of the line for the Ontario Northland Railway, lies on the Moose River near James Bay.

Floatplane waits at Norway House, northeast of Lake Winnipeg, to fly an Indian baby home from the hospital. Hudson's Bay Company outposts still link the bush with civilization. Feverish with pneumonia, a three-year-old Eskimo child arrives at Churchill for treatment after a 400-mile flight from Baker Lake.

RALPH GRAY, NATIONAL GEOGRAPHIC STAFF

NATIONAL GEOGRAPHIC PHOTOGRAPHERS DAVID S. BOYER (LOWER LEFT) AND WINFIELD PARKS

"About 2,500 people live in the trading area of our two stores. We're primarily storekeepers now, but we still trade for furs when a bunch of pelts comes in."

That evening we visited Hank and Walter Buhr, his district manager at the time. The wooden Archway Building stood before us, one of two original structures. Built in 1826, it was the key unit in a quadrangle that became a fort when a thick door shut across the archway. Treading in the footsteps of Sir George Simpson, the Company's greatest governor, and Sir John Franklin,

Arctic explorer who used such posts as jumping-off places, we walked through the arcade and across the compound.

Mr. Buhr explained, "Company posts were often called this or that House, because they were the only buildings in the area. Norway House was named for a party of Norwegians sent out to construct a winter road inland from York Factory on Hudson Bay in 1814. The post lay on the main supply line in the war against the North West Company."

We discussed how geography had shaped

115

Canada's development. Two waterways led European vessels deep into Canada—the St. Lawrence estuary, and Hudson Bay. The French early made the St. Lawrence a Gallic stream, leaving the less hospitable northern route to the English. But even in Hudson Bay the French had a hand.

"It was two French renegades, you know, who were responsible for establishing the Hudson's Bay Company," Mr. Buhr said. "Groseilliers and Radisson found that the source of most of the furs flowing to Montreal was in the forests of the Cree. When the French governor wouldn't license them to trap in this area, they went anyway. They returned with a staggering harvest of furs, but their fines almost equaled their profits.

"Failing to recover their fortunes from the French, they went to Charles II of England and told him that Hudson Bay offered the most efficient means for tapping the Eldorado of furs, and that men operating from there would drain the supply away from the French.

"Thus the Hudson's Bay Company was born in 1670," Mr. Buhr continued. "Groseilliers, or 'Mr. Gooseberry' as the English called him, regained his wilderness paradise three years after John Milton published *Paradise Lost*—just to give you an idea of the age of my company. We established York Factory to serve this area. If you went to the outlet of Little Playgreen Lake and started drifting with the current of the Nelson River you'd end up on Hudson Bay not far from York Factory."

"I'd like to go to the outlet," I said. Next

Ivory spear eternally poised, a hunter carved in soapstone stalks Arctic prey. Massive strength of "Spearman" belies its actual size—just under 11 inches. At left, a Banks Island Eskimo admires a polar bear pelt. A housewife fleshes such a skin with an ulu. *Eskimos also use this tool in eating. Gripping meat tightly between the teeth, a diner slices off a bite with a sharp downward stroke.*

"THE ARCHER" BY NIVIAKSIAK
PRINTED BY IYOLA

day John Robertson showed up with his boat, saying he understood that I wanted to feel the current of the Nelson.

John was one of "the people," as the Indians call themselves. Some are Métis, descendants of Indian mothers and Scottish, English, or French fathers. Will and Donna joined us in the boat and listened with delight as John spun tales of the places we passed: "Drunken Island," where York boatmen were put ashore with a keg of rum to celebrate after a hard voyage; "Bull Island," where a bull which had gored a man was tied and burned to death; "Dog Island," where trappers let their sled dogs run in summer; "Hope Island," site of an abandoned school whose founders had hoped it would be self-sufficient by growing its own crops and raising livestock.

Eventually we found ourselves in a maze of islands and channels and felt the tug of a slight current.

"This is the outlet," John said.

Rain started falling and Donna crawled under a tarpaulin lying in the boat, but Will and I sat it out, imagining ourselves slaving on a York boat as the current of the mighty Nelson pulled at the craft.

When we returned, drenched and shivering, Max Paupanekis, another of "the

SYMBOLS ON THE PRINTS: ARCH SERVES AS TRADEMARK FOR WEST BAFFIN ESKIMO CO-OPERATIVE; ARTISTS' SIGNATURES APPEAR IN ESKIMO CHARACTERS.

Compelling sense of life pervades the art of Eskimos on Baffin Island. To produce such prints as "Geese Frightened by Fox," an artist carves a low-relief design into a slab of polished soapstone, then delicately inks it and presses paper against the surface. Eskimos created "Four Muskoxen" and "The Archer" by stippling color through stencils cut from sealskin.

"FOUR MUSKOXEN" BY OSHAWEETUK

119

people," told me about York boats, built at York Factory not just for hauling furs but for building a nation.

"The first settlers of the Red River valley came through here with all their freight," Max said. "York boats had a crew of eight to fifteen, and could carry up to four tons of cargo. All but two of the crew bent to the sweeps, the steersman stood at the cumbersome rudder, and the man in the bow studied the waters ahead."

Our floatplane returned the following day and we boarded for the flight south to Winnipeg. We landed on the Red River—a brown current that snakes across Manitoba's green, treeless plains.

Metropolitan Winnipeg, the provincial capital with its 523,000 persons, seemed like New York to us bush rats. From our hotel we could see Hudson's Bay House, Canadian headquarters of the Company. Nearer at hand stood the gate of Upper Fort Garry,

120

DOM NAJOLIA

all that remained of the strong point around which Winnipeg grew at the junction of the Red and the Assiniboine Rivers.

Winnipeg was not new to us, for my wife was born here. After a few days of sightseeing we decided to push north again. This time we would go all the way to Churchill on Hudson Bay.

One might think a train would be the last form of transportation available for such a journey, but the Canadian National Rail-

ways in 1929 had pushed a line across the muskeg to the northern Manitoba port, 978 miles away.

"Taking the sleeper to Churchill is one of the unique railroad experiences in North America," friends in Winnipeg told us. "You can sip refreshments in the lounge while watching the sun and the last three cars sink slowly into the muskeg."

Before reaching the swampy woods, however, our train curved leisurely west and then turned north through a long, golden prairie evening to Dauphin.

During the night, I awoke to find the train stopped in a station named Hudson Bay. In our roundabout route, we had crossed into Saskatchewan. At this junction, wheat of the western prairies feeds into the rail line and eventually reaches the great grain elevator at Churchill.

Next morning the train rolled back into Manitoba and across the spruce-matted sponge that covers the northern part of the province. All day and all night the tracks followed a swath cut through the woods, skirting lakes, crossing rivers, and bisecting Indian villages. The "muskeg express" swung so far north that we found it still twilight when we turned in at 11 p.m. Sunrise came at about 3:30. Then, at breakfast, just south of Churchill, we noticed that the trees flying by the windows were smaller and scarcer. Stretches of bare, rocky terrain slid past. Soon the trees disappeared almost completely. We had entered the Barren Lands—subarctic tundra that stretches to the Arctic.

At Churchill, hundreds of miles beyond the reach of Manitoba's highway system, a covey of taxis met our train. They had been shipped in to serve the two hotels and, incredibly enough, a motel. From our window

in the two-story Hudson Hotel we looked out at the 5,000,000-bushel grain elevator at the mouth of the Churchill River.

Home styles in Churchill townsite range from early packing crate to late aluminum. No householders have planted trees; few attempt to grow lawns, because of the harsh climate and lack of suitable soil.

We walked across boulders and a sand beach to the shore of Hudson Bay. About half a mile out, blue water ended at a brilliant white wall of pack ice. Floe ice broke off and drifted to shore. I checked my pock-

et calendar: July 2! Yet the first ship from Europe would not plow through for three weeks. After a ten-week shipping season, the ice would close in again.

Some of the white spots in the water seemed to appear and disappear. We realized these were Churchill's famous beluga whales, miniature Moby Dicks sounding and blowing and showing their white backs for an instant. Hunting was restricted to local residents and their total catch limited. To capture the whales, Indians and Eskimos in motorboats herded them into

Fields of wheat reach to the horizon on the virtually treeless plains of Saskatchewan, where farmers cultivate 25 million acres. Looking no bigger than ants, combines head the grain near the community of Riceton, where a row of elevators awaits the crop. With headlamps lighting the way, the self-propelled harvesters work into the night.

shallow water or into nets. Until 1969 a whale factory, processing the 10- to 15-foot-long belugas, was one of Churchill's industries. But government provides the big payroll in Churchill itself, the Port of Churchill, the Eskimo village of Akudlik, H.M.C.S. *Churchill* (a naval communications center), and a rocket research range at Fort Churchill—each one an outreach of Winnipeg or Ottawa.

We talked with George Barnes and Wally Maduke, then managers of the local Hudson's Bay Company stores. "Not every visi-

tor is a potential customer," Wally told us. "Some of our most interesting citizens are polar bears. They drift ashore on ice floes and cut through town to reach the wilderness. Occasionally one lingers around the dump or pulls a fish out of a net at low tide."

By taxi we went to Akudlik, a thriving Eskimo village. Brought here from the Keewatin District far to the north for employment, many of the Eskimos liked their new surroundings and stayed. We strolled into the children's playground behind the homes, and Donna easily fell into games

*Eyes left and lances at "carry,"
Royal Canadian Mounted Police
perform the Musical Ride at Regina's Exhibition Grounds. The
touring troop of 32 horsemen trots
and canters in precision drill to
band music. Marksman draws a
bead outside the Regina barracks.
He wears a duty uniform — today's
Mounties reserve their scarlet
tunics for special ceremonies.*

*First Mounties drill at Lower Fort Garry, now a national his-
toric park near Winnipeg. Founded in 1873 as the North-West
Mounted Police, the force of fewer than 300 checked frontier
lawlessness and won the Indians' lasting trust. Today more
than 8,000 Mounties enforce Canada's federal laws.*

with several smiling, red-cheeked girls.

At Cape Merry, we walked half a mile across moss and summer flowers and under a canopy of dive-bombing insects to a ruined wall and an old powder magazine. From these relics of the French and English rivalry we looked across the mouth of the Churchill River to Eskimo Point and saw massive Fort Prince of Wales, one of the greatest monuments to colonial warfare in North America.

You can hire a canoe to visit those bleak ramparts—or a dog team in winter when ice bridges the river. But a swifter way opened up for me when I was invited on a helicopter flight to the fort.

The pilot landed on a rocky promontory in front of the lonely pile commanding the coast as well as the river. In 1732 the Hudson's Bay Company decided to build this bastion, and men labored on it until 1771, constructing walls 30 to 40 feet thick and mounting 42 cannon.

Eleven years later, La Pérouse, the French admiral-geographer, sailed up with 400 men in three ships. Samuel Hearne, Hudson's Bay Company governor, had only 39 men in the fort. He surrendered without a shot. The French destroyed the barracks and many of the guns but had little success in trying to blow up the outer walls.

Because Hearne had been an explorer-hero to me since my boyhood, I wanted to go to a place that recalled a more pleasant time in his life. I asked the pilot to hop over to Sloop's Cove.

Here Hearne had carved his name on a rock, shortly before his epic overland journey of 1770-72 across the Barren Lands to the Arctic coast and back. He was the first European to reach *ultima Thule* on foot.

Gazing at this historic stone, I realized that the farther north we had journeyed, the richer the history. A short flight bridged

Riding through a snow-whitened gully near High River, Alberta, cowboys haze Herefords and black crossbred steers on the EP Ranch, once owned by the Duke of Windsor. Millions of beef cattle range Canada's western grasslands.

Edmonton's changing skyline: Glowing initials identify the office building and depot of the Canadian National Railways. A corner of the City Hall glows brightly at right; high-rise apartments like the one at left may one day surround it. Northernmost major city in Canada, Edmonton is capital of the oil-rich Province of Alberta. Opposite, lawn bowlers play a leisurely match in the park around the Legislative Building. Here, only a century ago, guards warily shut the gates of Fort Edmonton when the Blackfoot Indians arrived in force; food and buffalo robes changed hands over the top of the 18-foot stockade walls.

A MARI USQUE AD MARE

Canada's coat of arms, adapted for a wall plaque, marshals the maple leaf at the base of its shield with symbols of four kingdoms: England's three lions, the lion rampant of Scotland, Ireland's harp, the lilies of France. The English lion and Scottish unicorn stand as supporters. Below runs the nation's motto, "From Sea to Sea."

Saskatchewan's Legislative Building — built in a free English Renaissance style — towers above Wascana Lake in Regina. Founded in 1882 by Canadian and European settlers, the "Queen City" of the plains today reigns as the commercial hub of Saskatchewan. Regina also boasts a lakeshore provincial center of 1,300 acres including picnic sites, playgrounds, and a concert hall.

Loucheux tribeswoman Anna Vaneltsi spent her winters trapping rabbits and selling the skins at Fort McPherson in the District of Mackenzie until her early nineties. Canada's Indians number nearly 225,000 and belong to about 50 tribes.

Locked in winter ice, the Slave River meanders through a watery wilderness of muskeg. In the summer of 1789 Alexander Mackenzie, 25-year-old Scottish fur trader and explorer, rode this chill trail north by birch-bark canoe to Great Slave Lake, then coursed to the Arctic Ocean on the wide stream that today bears his name.

RICHARD W. MONTAGUE

the centuries as the helicopter returned to Fort Churchill, a center devoted to upper-atmosphere research.

Fort Churchill was chosen because it lies close to the northern focal point of the earth's magnetic field, where auroral activity is greatest, and near the Arctic breeding grounds for weather.

From the Blockhouse I watched an Arcas launch. The rocket, only six feet long, quickly zoomed from sight, its nose cone carrying instruments to record temperatures and wind velocities in the ionosphere.

The Canadian north, like the Australian outback, is really one widely scattered community where everyone seems to know everyone else. Thus I had heard of Ernie Senior, enthusiastic spokesman for the region and editor and publisher of the *Taiga Times,* long before arriving in Churchill. I called him, and he sent his teen-age son for me. So it was that I rode on the back of a Honda to Ernie's book-filled home to make my official call on the unofficial mayor of Churchill.

Mr. Senior was conducting half a dozen crusades at once—all with the idea of a better day ahead for Churchill. He wasn't thinking in terms of garden clubs or even of paved streets, but rather: all-weather

highways to Winnipeg and to Yellowknife, capital of the Northwest Territories ... submarine freighters to haul wheat out of Churchill all year ... thermonuclear power to heat the waters of Hudson Bay and keep it ice-free ... a reflector satellite to beam light and warmth to earth during the long northern winter ... a University of the North at Churchill.

"We know more about the South Pole than we know about Hudson Bay," he said. "A university would serve as a center for scientific study of the world's second-largest inland sea, a Canadian Mediterranean that is now practically disregarded as an economic asset. Instead of having four or five thousand people, Churchill could be a city of 50,000."

I left Mr. Senior and walked down the gravel street so dazed and thoughtful that several black flies chewed on me unheeded. Rarely have I met a booster of his caliber.

A bit of the future had already reached The Pas and Flin Flon, our next stops. The first grew up as a fur-trading crossroads.

"Next time you come this way, The Pas will be a big city," Jack Hone, a merchant, told me. "Power from a new dam on the Nelson River will run a large sawmill here and establish a lumber industry on the Saskatchewan River."

From The Pas, we swung north by bus to Flin Flon to take part in the annual Trout Festival, a riotous conclave of trappers, woodsmen, miners, Indians, and visitors that recalls the early rip-roaring days. An ore strike was made here in 1915. Prospectors, so the story goes, named their claims for one Josiah Flintabbatey Flonatin, hero of an old novel, who found a gold-studded hole leading from an underground lake.

In 1927 the Hudson Bay Mining and Smelting Company began operations, and today the property yields more than 80

Wolf pelts of dun and silver hang from the fur cache of prospector Gus Kraus on the South Nahanni River in the Northwest Territories. Used in trimming winter garments, the skins of these predators also bring a government bounty.

million dollars a year from slab zinc, metallic cadmium, refined copper, selenium, gold, silver, and lead concentrates.

The raw log-cabin camp of the early years now boasts paved streets, a golf course, tours of the smelters, a Lions Club, a curling rink, a hospital, a wildfowl sanctuary, and 10,200 people (plus another thousand just across the border in Saskatchewan). Flin Flon showed me that a few short years can bring the good life to the towns of the north.

T HE CANADIAN SHIELD that holds Flin Flon's fabulous ores once stood as an inhospitable barrier between eastern and western Canada. Today, however, the tapping of the area's vast wealth of minerals, forests, and water power has become a unifying force for the nation.

The great rivers that once carried the voyageurs now promise power unlimited. In eastern Manitoba engineers will divert the Churchill into the Nelson and the combined waters will produce a million kilowatts at the Kettle Rapids project. And between the places of the water spreads the endless carpet of trees—barely touched.

Again we flew south to Winnipeg. This time we headed west, driving along the Trans-Canada Highway toward Regina, capital of Saskatchewan.

This "Queen City" of the plains was named for Victoria Regina, Queen of England. Before getting its majestic name in 1882, the spot was known as Pile of Bones.

In presettlement years the area had been a favored hunting ground of the Indians, who drove buffalo herds into compounds built beside a creek. Bones of the animals accumulated, hence the name.

When settlers arrived they put up a few sod houses. Later, the Canadian Pacific's tracks reached the spot, and in 1882 the North-West Mounted Police made the city their headquarters.

The Mounties! Those scarlet-coated men quickly brought law and order to the wilderness—and fame to Regina. In 1920 the force moved its headquarters to Ottawa, and acquired a new name—the Royal

133

Riven by a towering pillar of limestone, wild water thunders 316 feet at Virginia Falls, highest in the Northwest Territories. Adventurous boatmen, like the one at lower right, challenge the roiling

whirlpools and treacherous rapids of the South Nahanni River to reach the great eddying pool below this remote cataract. In places, sheer cliffs of the rock-strewn gorge soar as high as 2,000 feet.

135

Canadian Mounted Police. But Regina retained a recruit training center that today welcomes an unending stream of visitors from the United States.

When the force was established in 1873, however, it did *not* welcome certain Americans in the vast hunting ground between the Great Lakes and the Rockies where 30,000 Indians followed the buffalo. Fortune hunters and desperadoes drifted across the border, selling firewater to the tribesmen and wantonly attacking them.

The first action of the Mounties was to locate and destroy Fort Whoop-up, stronghold of the whiskey runners. As my family and I drove toward Regina, we roughly paralleled part of the force's epic ride, in 1874, across almost treeless plains to the junction of the Bow and Belly Rivers in what is now southern Alberta.

The Mounties reached Fort Whoop-up ragged and weary, their horses spent. But their reputation had gone before them,

and they found the stockade nearly deserted. Nearby they established their own strong point, Fort Macleod, the force's first post in the territories. Never again would lawlessness go unchecked in Canada.

The Indian recognized the Mountie as his friend; the scarlet tunic signified fair dealing. Because he trusted the "red coats," Crowfoot, chief of the Blackfoot confederacy, signed the most important Indian peace treaty in Canadian history.

"The advice given me and my people has proved to be very good," Crowfoot said. "Bad men and whisky were killing us. . . . The police have protected us as the feathers of the bird protect it from the frosts of winter."

I confess that I myself have never felt better protected than when we reached Regina and drove out to the Mounties' Barracks, where we saw young men undergoing rigorous training.

Donna immediately wanted to go to the

stables to see the horses. "You're in luck," said Sgt. Roy Richards of Newfoundland, who took time off to show us around. "This is the final summer for using horses in our training program. In effect, the Mounties have been dismounted for years. My job is a sign of the times. I'm in charge of driver training here."

While watching recruits put the beautifully groomed chargers through their paces, we learned that to get their man nowadays, Mounties rely on the steering wheel rather than the reins. They also depend on a small navy and a fleet of planes.

Along with his horse, the Mountie has lost his other world-famed trademark, the

Blood staining his coat, a wounded polar bear fights attacking dogs on Banks Island in the Northwest Territories. A bullet killed the great beast but not before he mauled one of his tormentors. Below, an Eskimo hunter scouts a frozen sea for holes in the ice where seals surface to breathe. When he makes a kill, he takes the meat home to his family and uses the blubber to feed his dog team and to bait bear traps.

dazzling red tunic, now worn only for full dress or ceremonial occasions. In addition, the broad-brimmed hat, high boots, and spurs proved impractical in a highway patrol car. Door frames knocked off the peaked hats, and spurs sometimes snagged on the gas pedal.

For everyday duty the Mountie now wears a brown jacket, blue trousers, black shoes, and a forage cap. But the glamor remains. The Mountie is the image of Canada, the only policeman in the world who stands as the symbol of his country.

Nowhere can you better appreciate the tradition and lore of the Royal Canadian Mounted Police than in the post Chapel and Museum at the Regina Barracks. Originally a canteen, the Chapel came to Regina

in sections via railroad, river steamer, and oxcart in 1885. Nine years later the Commissioner's wife suggested it be converted into a place of worship.

The Museum, a mélange of faded flags, historic paintings, and every imaginable kind of memorabilia, can hold you spellbound for hours.

My eyes fell on a strange-looking ring. A card beside it stated that Constable Clarence Loasby made it from a Cree bullet that plowed through his body and lodged in his clothing during the Louis Riel rebellion in 1885. Miraculously surviving, Loasby wore the ring until he died in 1936.

We stepped back to today in the sunlight of the Square, where recruits drill endlessly. The sturdy, spotless buildings scattered

Late-October sun bronzes wind-driven snow at Sachs Harbour, where some 70 Eskimos live in one of the world's northernmost communities. Their frame houses—the only habitations on Banks Island—rest on oil-drum foundations atop permafrost a thousand feet deep. Summer transforms the land, setting it ablaze with flowering plants and ferns. Self-sufficient residents hunt caribou, seal, hare, and ptarmigan, and fish lakes and rivers for trout and whitefish. Here the Arctic Ocean offers only a meager catch.

Crossbreed pups treasured by Peter Sydney will become members of a nine-dog sled team. No pampered pets, they eat once a day and must sleep outdoors in any weather. Eskimos customarily name their dogs after deceased members of the family.

139

across pleasant lawns make "barracks" seem a harsh word to describe this police college on the outskirts of Regina.

Regina fits our idea of how big a city should be. We climbed to the roof of the tallest building and could see far into the plains beyond.

More than any other direction, Will and I found ourselves looking northwest. That had been the trend of this trip and indeed of Canada's growth.

Once before we had followed the northwestward course of empire from Regina to Edmonton to the Peace River to Great Slave Lake, but this time we would go on only in memory or vicariously.

Piercing the almost unthinkable distances with the mind's eye, we recalled the thrill of coming on amber-hued Alexandra Falls thundering in the wilderness. That night we all had a good laugh when Will rolled out of bed because the floor of our hotel room in Hay River slanted sharply where the building's foundations had settled unevenly into the permafrost.

THEN THERE WAS THE TIME I took the ice supply boat out of Yellowknife and spent the night on Great Slave Lake, on a barge where men packed whitefish and lake trout into ice-filled boxes for shipment to Chicago, Detroit, and New York. Later, I flew to Fort Smith and on to Fort Chipewyan on Lake Athabasca. There a Chinese served me hot soup and a young sergeant of the Royal Canadian Corps of Signals took me to the site of the old post where Mackenzie wintered before setting out for the Arctic and Pacific Oceans.

"In Chip they still talk about how your plane flew low over the buffalo in Wood Buffalo National Park and spooked them toward the Slave River," my young friend Richard W. Montague once told me.

Dick is an example of the countless adventurers still answering the call of Canada's northern waters. One summer he put in near Jasper National Park, and headed by canoe for the Arctic Ocean. He paddled north down the Athabasca River—risking his life in its Grand Rapids—to Lake Atha-

basca, down the Slave to Great Slave Lake, and down the Mackenzie River to the remote Eskimo and Indian settlement of Aklavik—more than 2,000 miles.

Not long ago the South Nahanni called Dick back to the Northwest Territories. "Among the Canadian rivers I've seen—and there have been some wild ones—none is so treacherous as the South Nahanni," Dick said. "More than a dozen men have vanished in its rocky fastnesses.

"I drove the Alaska Highway to Fort Nelson, British Columbia, chartered a plane to Nahanni Butte, and started up the Nahanni with Donald Turner in his 'river snake,' a 30-foot, snub-nosed boat designed for swift, churning water.

"Canyon walls rose 2,000 feet on either side of the plunging river, carved with pink formations that reminded me of Bryce Canyon, Utah. Our two 33-horsepower outboards needed all their strength to push us through the Figure Eight Rapids, 'the rapids which run both ways.'

"After two days and 120 miles of rough going, we rounded a bend in a winding canyon, heard the boom of a cataract, and looked directly into a wall of water, water to the skyline! We had reached Virginia Falls, the continent's most pristine, remote, and fabulous waterfall.

"Estimates vary as to whether Canada contains one-third or one-fourth of the world's fresh water, but it seemed that all of it was pouring down in front of me, a sense-shattering curtain 316 feet high.

"I thought of Albert Faille, Raymond M. Patterson, John Lentz, and the other adventurers who had reached this spot before me. But while I watched, I felt that this waterfall was mine."

I know the feeling; Will and I still think of Alexandra Falls as ours.

That's Canada for you. There's a river, a lake, an island, a waterfall for everyone.

Wolverine fur wreathes the face of an Eskimo boy at Sachs Harbour. At age six the children leave their island home for school in mainland Canada, returning to their families only in summer.

ROCKIES

The silent mountain grandeur,
the challenge of adventure,
the ancient mystery of creation

BY ALAN PHILLIPS

THOUGH still below the timber line, I found that my breathing had become labored as I followed my guide up the switchbacks of a sheep trail. Shale became limestone. Then a steep ridge confronted us and we climbed with hands and feet. We paused and I looked back, down a sheer drop to the green-white ribbon of Cameron Creek. A feeling of awe and exhilaration swept over me. I had a sense of challenge and of adventure, as if I were on the threshold of discovery.

I stood on Mount Crandell, part of the eastern escarpment of the Canadian Rockies, familiar around the world through picture postcards. I had driven west into Waterton Lakes National Park on the Alberta-Montana border the day before, to begin a tour of these mountains. My car had emerged from a coulee scented with wild rose, and this escarpment, still snow-slabbed at June's end, had loomed abruptly from the plains of Alberta, a huge jagged wall. I could imagine the barrier it presented to 18th-century fur traders.

It still seemed to guard what mountaineers call "the mystery of the beyond." For

Cascade Mountain lifts a snow-powdered summit above Banff, Alberta. Skirting town, Bow River flows past castlelike Banff Springs Hotel, one of the world's largest mountain-resort inns.

143

despite the annual influx of some four million visitors the Canadian Rockies remain one of the great wilderness regions.

All around me rose peaks and precipices streaked and creviced with ice and snow, a world of timeless grandeur accessible only on foot, by pack horse, or by helicopter. Mountains stretch far to the west, and in a series of summits buckle northward almost a thousand miles to the Liard River, just south of the Yukon Territory.

These Canadian mountains do not tower

Bull moose wades twilit Cameron Lake, and a young mule deer peers from foliage glistening with dew in Waterton-Glacier International Peace Park, shared by Canada and the U.S.

as high as the Rockies in the United States. But the river valleys have the narrow V-shape that indicates youth, and above the timber line soar great reaches of rock and snow, breathtaking, spectacular, dramatic.

In all their length there is not a single city. Their few small towns lie along the

roads and rail lines of five passes. They have never had a big gold strike to open them. Their only important resources are coal, gas and oil, wood and water—and scenery as it was before man came.

The entire region of these Rockies is a vast recreational area, an unsurpassed adventure-land made up of five federal parks. Four of them form one great complex: Kootenay, Banff, Yoho, and Jasper. Together with Waterton, the parks encompass more than 8,000 square miles.

In such an immense outdoor region, climbers must follow strict regulations. Before setting out on so simple a climb as Mount Crandell I had notified park branch headquarters in the village of Waterton Park. If I failed to return on schedule, a warden would check back over the route. The wardens act as policemen, firemen, and caretakers, and all have training in mountain rescue work and first aid.

My guide was chief park warden Frank Camp, young, lithe, and alert. The Rockies to him seem less a place than a way of life, and like so many wardens he is an amateur botanist. He led me through a knee-high forest of full-grown pine, through meadows of brilliant flowers, over rocks embossed green, orange, and black with lichen. Now one last ridge, a short incline, and

the summit: 7,812 feet. We had climbed from a temperate to an arctic zone, in effect going 1,200 miles north in four hours. Before us lay high lakes, frozen waterfalls, sparkling snowfields cradled in rock.

Overhead an eagle soared, and six bighorn sheep eyed us from a ridge. On the blue-green Waterton Lakes that shimmered into the mist of Montana, a launch crawled toward Glacier National Park. Together the two connecting parks form the International Peace Park, set up by Canada and the United States in 1932.

For several days I toured this vast memorial to the friendship of two nations. All along the roads signs read: "For your own safety do not approach or feed the bears." Black bears usually create no problem, but those fed on scraps often become a nuisance. The Rockies are also a stronghold of the powerful grizzly. One blow of its huge forearm can break a bull's neck.

A man who knows grizzlies well is Andy Russell, a flamboyant naturalist-photographer. Leaving Waterton for Kootenay Park on the far side of the Rockies, a five-hour drive, I stopped at the hilltop house he calls Hawk's Nest. His guns, books, and trophies lined the walls.

A big, long-haired man with a deep tan, Russell had just completed a book, *Grizzly*

JAMES L. STANFIELD, BLACK STAR

Saddlemaker Steve Cody tools western saddles on a ranch near Banff. Hollywood heroes have ridden into the sunset astride his handiwork. Sculptor Charlie Beil of Banff once punched steers and wrangled horses for a livelihood. "I've lived it all," he says. "Now I cast it in bronze." Examples of his work have been presented to Queen Elizabeth II and to a former President of Mexico, Adolfo López Mateos.

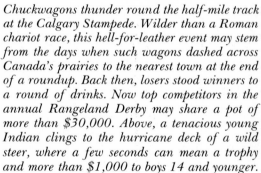

Chuckwagons thunder round the half-mile track at the Calgary Stampede. Wilder than a Roman chariot race, this hell-for-leather event may stem from the days when such wagons dashed across Canada's prairies to the nearest town at the end of a roundup. Back then, losers stood winners to a round of drinks. Now top competitors in the annual Rangeland Derby may share a pot of more than $30,000. Above, a tenacious young Indian clings to the hurricane deck of a wild steer, where a few seconds can mean a trophy and more than $1,000 to boys 14 and younger.

Country. He had been stalking and filming grizzlies for three years.

"The second year we stopped carrying guns and started getting more pictures," he said, implying that a grizzly can sense danger. "One day a mother and two cubs charged us. But we stood our ground—I've got pictures of hair coming up on a grizzly's back. A shout stopped them. Then we stepped aside, and they went on their way.

"Why did they stop? Here's an animal that everything has run from for thousands of years, and when you don't run, maybe it throws him out of gear."

A grizzly never attacks unless alarmed or provoked, and turns vicious only when ill, Russell claimed. "They're more tolerant of us than we are of them," he said. "They know how to enjoy life better than we do. I'll never forget one big old grizzly sliding down a snowfield on Crandell, half a ton of bear tobogganing down the mountain. Then he'd go back up, look at the scenery, put up a paw, scratch his ear, and take off again on his rump with his foot still up."

I drove north through pastureland patched with aspen and cottonwood. White-face cattle stood in fields of high grass

fragrant with clover. Along every creek a gravel road wound into the eastern ranges, each leading to natural-gas fields linked to the world's longest pipeline, running 2,145 miles to Ontario. Another line carries gas 1,500 miles to California.

I passed small wooden ranch houses with horses in log corrals, and curved into the cattle center of Pincher Creek. The town had that old-west look compounded of weathered siding and hitching posts, but on its dusty streets the clatter of hoofs merged with the sound of car engines.

This is the land of the chinook, a phe-nomenal wind from the west that sweeps across the Rockies. It screams through the passes, reaching speeds as high as 100 miles an hour. As it spills down the eastern slopes, the wind, heated by compression, rushes onto the prairie so hot and dry in January that pussy willows may begin to bloom and bears leave their dens.

Overnight a chinook can jump the tem-perature 50°, licking a foot of snow off the range, baring the grass for cattle. It's the Rockies' zany chinook that makes the prov-ince such fine cattle country and imbues Albertans with zestful optimism.

149

The hub of Alberta's cattle empire lies in Calgary, just east of the Rockies in the high plains. Each July the city stages the Calgary Exhibition and Stampede, several days of hoop-la beginning with a parade of cowboys, cowgirls, Mounties, and Indians.

But aside from such engaging madness, the cowtown has changed. Since the first gusher at the Leduc field in 1947, Alberta has become the pulsing heart of Canada's great petroleum industry. Now Calgary and its northern rival—Edmonton, the provincial capital—are growing faster than any other metropolitan area in the nation.

Farther north, oil is being scooped from

Matterhorn of the Rockies, Mount Assiniboine towers 11,870 feet at the Continental Divide. On Lake Magog fog drifts like a phantom glacier. Skiers reach Assiniboine Lodge (right) after a two-day trip from Banff by jeep and horseback.

open-pit mines! Near Fort McMurray, Athabasca tar sand, black and heavy with crude oil, is lifted by bucket-wheel excavator for processing at a huge new $250,000,000 plant. Covering thousands of square miles in depths up to 200 feet, the sands may store as much as 600 *billion* barrels of oil.

From chinook country I drove to high, forested ridges and into Crowsnest Pass,

150

winding alongside the southern spur of the Canadian Pacific Railway. Huge hills of coal flashed past, small towns grimy with coal dust, incongruous under the glistening snow of the crags towering above. Vast seams of soft coal stretch more than 700 miles north of Crowsnest, one of the greatest deposits in the British Commonwealth.

At Crowsnest Lake a sign marked the Continental Divide, 4,457 feet. Alberta Route 3 had become British Columbia Route 3. I dropped down through country famed for its game—elk, bighorn, moose, grizzly, cougar—into that strange broad valley called the Rocky Mountain Trench.

The trench, two to more than ten miles wide, separates the Rockies from the older western ranges of British Columbia. A major break in the earth's crust, it runs the length of the Canadian Rockies. Geologists do not agree on its origin, but many anthropologists think the trench may have served as a corridor south for prehistoric men after they crossed the Bering Strait from Asia.

The road ran north along the Kootenay River and the high, timbered ridges of the Rockies. Cattle grazed on slopes sprinkled with sage and fir, a dry belt known as Skookumchuck prairie. On my left the mountains bore no sign of habitation. Into lonely green clefts old logging roads vanished, overgrown from disuse.

The highway climbed above blue-green Columbia Lake, the headwaters of the Columbia River, curved around Lake Windermere—glazed with the day's last sunlight—and branched off into the little village of Invermere.

Television sets glowed in the cabins of the Shuswap Indian Reserve as I drove north and right-angled on Highway 93 through a corridor of rocks. I passed through the needle's-eye gorge of Sinclair Canyon and the Iron Gates, the striking red-walled portal to Kootenay National Park, and checked into a pine-paneled motel room overlooking Radium Hot Springs.

In the morning, mist writhed off the "hot pool." I trotted down long wooden steps to a complex called the Aquacourt—two pools, coffee shop, sun deck, massage and locker

Intricate beadwork emblazons the regalia of 90-

rooms—around a mineral spring that issues hot from the mountainside.

Already a thousand people were soaking, chattering in many languages. Some, with arthritis and rheumatism, believed the waters might cure them. Most simply enjoyed the scenery around them, the flowers, and each other's company.

Next day, as I drove along the Banff-Windermere Highway, a bear ambled out

ear-old Chief Sitting Eagle of the Assiniboine, or Stoney, tribe during an annual festival at Banff.

of the bush. In Sinclair Pass a coyote loped across the road. Near the Kootenay River, I braked to avoid a sharp-tailed grouse. I left the Kootenay, picked up the Vermilion, and followed its rust-red banks into the main ranges. High on Mount Wardle three mountain goats moved in slow motion.

Now the road scaled the Continental Divide. Peaks reared above the glaciers, sculptured in tiers and turrets and scarred by the ice-carved basins called cirques. From every fold streams ran like silver threads. I drove out of British Columbia, back into Alberta, and into the Bow valley of Banff, the first of Canada's national parks.

This Canadian playground was promoted by U. S.-born William Cornelius Van Horne. In the 1880's, Van Horne pushed through the Rockies with the Canadian Pacific Railway — then one of the world's

Its lower slopes cloaked with spruce, fir, and lodgepole pine, sharp-ridged Mount Rundle tilts upward

,940 feet in Banff National Park. Vermilion Lakes fishermen cast for rainbow and eastern brook trout.

155

longest at 2,900 miles. When his workers discovered hot sulphur springs in the Bow valley, the government moved quickly to preserve ten square miles around them.

"Since we cannot export the scenery," Van Horne said, "we shall have to import the tourists." So he built an inn near Siding 29, later named Banff for Banffshire, the Scottish birthplace of George Stephen, first Canadian Pacific president. Alpinists from Europe were among passengers on the first trains, and when they saw these virgin peaks the invasion of Banff began—and has never ended.

Below cloud-wreathed Mount Eisenhower, once called Castle Mountain, I turned southeast into the ceaseless flow of the Trans-Canada Highway, a superbly banked corridor through a park that has now grown to 2,564 square miles. From all over Canada and the U. S., cars stream in and out, and when a bear or a deer blocks the road the tie-up can stretch for miles.

Behind a sightseeing bus I crawled across the CPR tracks into the flux of Canada's busiest small town. Cars choked Banff's wide main street. Sidewalks teemed with tourists. The architecture was characterless, but somehow nothing jarred. Above and all around loomed the crags and escarpments, muting everything, so near that even the neon signs seemed subdued.

High-riding derrickman on a drilling rig in Alberta helps roughnecks, far below, swing a string of drill pipe into the hole. The province leads Canada in oil production and soft-coal deposits. Grimy, grinning miner works a mountain seam near Crowsnest Pass on the Continental Divide. A geyser of sulphur sprays into a huge vat (below) at Pincher Creek, Alberta. After the sulphur cools and hardens, bulldozers break it up for loading into rail cars. Most will go into the making of fertilizer and sulphuric acid.

JAMES L. STANFIELD, BLACK STAR

I crossed a stone bridge over the Bow and there on a bend of the river rose the bulk of Van Horne's rebuilt inn, the 600-room Banff Springs Hotel. It dominates the landscape, a magnificent anachronism, seeking to rival the majesty of nature.

In the morning I had breakfast on Sulphur Mountain. A gondola lift takes visitors up half a mile in eight minutes. On the terrace of a tea house near the summit I sipped a hot drink and watched the spectacle changing with the light. Across the valley on Mount Norquay what looked like

yellow ants crawled up a long slash in the evergreens: A chair lift built for skiers was carrying summer sightseers to the top of Norquay's two-mile ski run.

As I hiked down Sulphur to the Bow River boathouse I saw a young girl sketching, one of 1,200 students attending the Banff School of Fine Arts on Tunnel Mountain. Banff is a mecca for artists, a Salzburg of the Rockies. And each summer session ends with a two-week tour program of music, dance, and drama in western Canada and the United States.

Trailing plumes of snow, skiers flash down a slope of Mount Temple in Banff National Park; the three in the foreground perform high-speed turns. Neighboring Lake Louise booms in winter, its lifts transporting guests to the tops of long, interconnected runs. Sunshine Village and its Inn (below) present an inviting island of warmth and comfort to weary experts and snow bunnies alike after the rigors of the icy world of Mount Bourgeau.

But this week of early July, Alberta's Indians staged the show. It began with some 30 Assiniboine, or Stoney, braves in feathers and beaded buckskins. Led by two Mounties, they rode their ponies down main street, shaking their rattles and staring with deadpan faces at the tourists.

The Indian Days celebration dates from 1889, when floods washed out the CPR tracks leading from Banff. The inn manager hired local Indians to entertain his stranded guests with horse races. Indians and visitors had so much fun that the contests became an annual event. Almost a thousand Stoney, Sarcee, Cree, and Blackfoot now drive in, hauling their horses by trailer. They pitch their tepees and put on a four-day rodeo. In the evening tourists join them in tribal dances.

I browsed in the Banff Indian Trading Post, stocked with native handicraft—moccasins, buckskins, tribal rattles, furs, and a headdress of eagle feathers. Beside the Bow, I studied large water-carved rocks called hoodoos, four lumpy statue-like figures. Then I rejoined the traffic on the

Trans-Canada, and headed for Lake Louise 36 miles northwest.

The peaks darkened and sharpened as I climbed toward the Divide, and the early evening air had an icy tingle. Around the great spike of Mount Temple I could see a white swirl of snow, and I felt no envy for the Alpine Club team from Japan that had come to Banff to climb the pinnacle.

I pulled up in front of Chateau Lake Louise, where buses discharge tour loads every five minutes. Next morning I walked out French doors onto the terrace facing the lake. Red, white, and yellow poppies nodded in the breeze. Green lawn sloped to the sapphire blue of the lake. From its farther shore dark, timbered mountains rose and parted to reveal the glacier glittering on Mount Victoria.

From Lake Louise the Trans-Canada Highway runs west through Yoho National Park, a hiker's paradise, where I lunched in a field of buttercups beside Emerald Lake. I stood in the spray of Takakkaw Falls, highest in Canada, cascading 1,200 feet from Daly Glacier. Yoho merits its name: a Cree Indian exclamation of wonder.

East of the village of Field, the park headquarters, I stopped to train-watch. The famous Spiral Tunnels that pierce Cathedral Mountain and Mount Ogden make this the most contorted track on the continent. The silver transcontinental "Canadian" came laboring up the slope, disappearing and reappearing as it looped under Cathedral. The long CPR freights, even with the tunnels, need four engines to push and pull them up the grade.

From Yoho I backtracked to Lake Louise and turned north on the Banff-Jasper Highway, one of the most spectacular scenic routes in North America. I followed the Bow, the Mistaya, and the North Sas-

katchewan Rivers around peaks rearing ever higher, ever sharper. The glaciers merged in an icecap, choking every valley with snow.

The road climbed the shoulder of Mount Athabasca, crossed the meadows of Sunwapta Pass, 6,675 feet high, and there just beside the road a river of ice flowed down from a skyline white with the accumulated snow of centuries.

I stopped for the night at a small chalet on a meadow beside the road. I had reached the Columbia Icefield, the largest body of glacial ice in the Rockies. For more than 100 square miles it encrusts the peaks and smothers the crevices of the highest mountains. From this vast deep freeze, ice melt flows to three oceans: down into the North Saskatchewan River to Hudson Bay and the Atlantic; into the Columbia River to the Pacific; and down Athabasca Glacier into the Sunwapta, the Athabasca, the Slave,

RICHARD W. MONTAGUE

High above a glacial valley near Lake Louise, a climber rappels the sheer drop of Devil's Thumb. His rope bisects 11,230-foot Mount Lefroy. A more expert mountaineer (right) balances on a cliff in Jasper National Park, Alberta. A moment later the bighorn dashed up a 60-degree slope.

161

and the Mackenzie Rivers to the Arctic.

I looked out in the morning on Athabasca Glacier, a broad gravel-stained tongue of ice lapping a lake brown with rock dust. The glacier was melting faster than it was moving forward. On either side, as if left by some giant bulldozer, lay embankments of rock and gravel called moraines. The mile-wide area beside the road looked like a mine-slag dump, scraped bare of vegetation, dull-gray, desolate—our world as the Ice Age glaciers had left it.

After breakfast I drove up a long moraine for a ride on the icefield. Warden Max Winkler, a gentle titan from Bavaria, joined me. Hunched in a snowmobile, we jolted down onto the glacier.

The ice river stretches about four miles, seamed and ridged, etched by scores of streams. In the center we stopped, and Max and I got out to explore on foot. The wind keened off the icecap, whipping snow from the peaks. I shivered despite my jacket; it was instant winter in midsummer.

From the icefield north, the highway threads the snow-frosted peaks of the

Lake O'Hara fills a glacier-carved bowl close under the Continental Divide in Yoho National Park, British Columbia. Visitors come on foot, horseback, or by bus to fish and to hike the miles of forested trails. Wandering tattler, a summer resident of northwest Canada, wades along lakeshores, feeding on insects and crustaceans.

Rockies' largest game sanctuary, Jasper National Park. At rainbow-draped Sunwapta Falls I watched browsing elk, huge creatures with antlers four feet across.

The road picked up the Athabasca, a merry river, purling through its wide wooded valley. The majestic snow-white dome of Mount Edith Cavell came into view, "the

Mountain of the Grand Crossing." For 50 years of the last century this Athabasca valley was the sole route across the mountains for the fur brigades.

In the early days of the fur trade, weary travelers sighed with relief when they sighted the solitary cabin of Jasper Hawse, a big fair-haired North West Company factor. There they could count on brook trout or buffalo steak for supper. Jasper vanished on a raft in the rapids of the Fraser River, but his name and his reputation for hospitality remain.

The village of Jasper is smaller and quieter than Banff. Deer saunter on the streets and make the rounds of the restaurants in

the morning. Nearby, on the manicured shores of Beauvert Lake spreads the Canadian National Railways' answer to CPR's Banff Springs: 53 cottages built around an elegant lodge. A traveler can still get brook trout. And sometimes the lodge serves buffalo steak when the parks branch is thinning out its herds. The CNR insists that the Athabasca route is still the only way to cross the continent.

From the front porch of my richly rustic bungalow I looked out on a wilderness

Canadian Pacific freight rounds Mount Stephen in British Columbia. Snowsheds guard trains from avalanches, but keeping switches unfrozen can bring a man face to face with a blizzard.

unchanged since Jasper Hawse's day. The last time I stayed here, two bears appeared on the lakeshore below. They stood erect, squared off, and sparred like clumsy but spirited boxers.

"The bears are unbelievable," said Ted Van Dyke, the hotel manager. "Last year a

164

Flowers abound in the high country, bright moments in the realm of glaciers. Pale mountain avenses edge a lake in Jasper National Park, and Indian paint brush glows red beside a fallen tree at Berg Lake, beneath Mount Robson. Monkshood of purple greets the short summer at Muncho Lake, near the Terminal Range. A bee sups at a western lousewort by Lake Louise, and the pink moss campion crowns a ridge next to the Columbia Icefield. Iceland poppies blossom in gardens near Chateau Lake Louise.

bus came in loaded with guests. Their bags were lining the sidewalk when along came a big black bear. He started down the line of luggage, sniffing it bag by bag. Halfway down he took a swipe with his paw and knocked a bag into the street. It broke open, spilling ladies' unmentionables all over. He sniffed through them and finally came up with a pound of cheese."

I walked to the golf course, where a bull

NATIONAL GEOGRAPHIC PHOTOGRAPHER JAMES P. BLAIR (LOWER RIGHT) AND JAMES L. STANFIELD, BLACK STAR

moose once took over the water hole. On the greens, bears turn on the sprinklers, and bull elk sometimes battle on the fairways. I visited the fish hatchery nearby, where mink, ducks, and ospreys raid the outdoor ponds and tanks. But the best show, I thought, takes place at the lodge dump, where black bears throw cans at each other, coyotes chase elk, and every freeloader backs away from the silvertip grizzly.

From Jasper north, trails penetrate untrammeled country for 50 miles, but from here to the Peace River highway, 250 miles, there is no road. I decided to go by plane from Edmonton, and I traveled east to the city in a glass-topped CNR coach that gave me a panoramic view as the mountains subsided to timbered foothills.

Next day, in a Piper Apache, I re-entered the Rockies along the Peace, an olive-green

167

rent in a rumpled blanket of bush. The only signs of human life were the smoke of logging camps and a barge towing a boom of logs. Then the river disappeared beneath an enormous mound of rock and sand that swarmed with earthmovers filling the gorge of the Peace, creating Portage Mountain Dam, 600 feet high and 1¼ miles long. By the mid-1970's its ten huge turbines will generate 2.3 million kilowatts, providing some of the cheapest power in Canada.

The river wound west for 75 miles, with the bush stretching back unbroken. My pilot flew through a pass and emerged in the Rocky Mountain Trench, where the Finlay and Parsnip Rivers collide to form the Peace. All this valley for 150 miles will vanish beneath the water backed up by the

dam. Soon these mountains will imprison 680 square miles of water, creating the biggest lake in British Columbia.

We followed the Finlay north past the few lonely houses called Fort Grahame. The river braided sandflats strewn with driftwood. The trench narrowed. We veered through a cleft in unnamed bare brown mountains, heading into what seemed a foam-flecked sea.

The sea became crags—gray, jagged, snow-veined, encrusted with glaciers. We banked east and the silvery glacial torrents broadened, browned, and branched through yellow-green muskeg speckled with caribou, that gentle roving reindeer, symbol of the north, which appears on the

Tumbling Glacier grinds down a flank of Mount Robson. Chunks of it, tons heavy, constantly crack away and splash into Berg Lake, named for its drifting blocks of ice. Passengers in a snowmobile get a memorable close-up of a crevasse of Athabasca Glacier, an arm of the Columbia Icefield. Melt from this huge reservoir of ice flows to the Pacific, Arctic, and Atlantic Oceans.

back of Canada's 25-cent coins. Then east again, over foothills and mesas. And beyond them the low flat sprawl of Fort Nelson, last supply center south of the Yukon Territory, bisected by a long straight khaki slash: the Alaska Highway.

A man with close-cropped hair watched me disembark. He studied me while I asked where I might find Dr. Gordon Taylor of the Geological Survey of Canada.

Taylor's camp, he said, was 160 miles west.

I had thought that Taylor would meet me, but the bush-ringed airport was empty. "How would I get there?"

"Phillips?" He had a quick tight grin. "I'm Gord Taylor."

In a truck with a stone-pitted windshield we drove a dusty highway lined with poplars and surfaced with soft shale that swells and grows greasy with rain. The road headed straight for the Rockies up the side of Steamboat Mountain, studded with trucks that had spun off the road in winter.

It plunged through cloud at Summit Lake, crossed the Racing and the Toad Rivers, shallow streams so swift that they cannot be forded even at knee-level.

We passed a motorcycle towing a boat, a truck lying wheels up, a helicopter stranded in a creek bed. "Ours," said Gord. "It broke down in flight and made an emergency landing. The country here is strewn with wrecks. Wind currents can be wicked."

We bordered the long deep-blue reach of Muncho Lake beside the sheer pale-gray wall of the Sentinel Range. At Mile 463—measured from Dawson Creek, British Columbia—we jolted off the highway onto gravel and rutted dry moss. Ravens flitted through stunted spruce sheltering a dozen white tents. Beside the lake sat a red-and-blue Bell helicopter. A sign read, "Geological Survey Rest Camp."

This was Operation Liard, a 16-man field party measuring and analyzing each rock bed lying between the Peace and Liard

JAMES L. STANFIELD, BLACK STAR

January's a joke to bathers in the 113° F. water of Radium Hot Springs. Indians once soaked here in a canyonside spring that surges from several vents. The slightly radioactive waters now fill two pools in British Columbia's Kootenay National Park. An enclosed Aquacourt offers a steam bath. At Jasper National Park two hungry mule deer, their horns in velvet, find a three-year-old friend with a ready handout. A roofless bus provides passengers with a neck-craning tour among lofty mountains in Waterton-Glacier International Peace Park.

With all outdoors as his laboratory, a scientist checks for clues to mineral wealth near the Rockies' Terminal Range. Camping in the wilderness for months at a time, 16 members of Canada's Geological Survey analyzed rock beds and charted a region spanning 40,000 square miles and 70 million years.

River of ice arcs below sharp summits of the Tower of London Range. Mount Stalin (right) rises above 9,000 feet. British Columbians named two other peaks in the province for Allied leaders of World War II. To the west, a mountain honors Winston Churchill; one to the northwest bears Franklin D. Roosevelt's name.

Rivers, 250 miles of mountains. For five years Taylor had backpacked among these peaks, coping with grizzlies, black flies, and flash floods to turn out the first detailed map of these northernmost Rockies.

"It's just one more piece in the jigsaw puzzle," he said. "Some day we may get the picture of what happened here 70 million years ago, when the Rockies were born."

After supper I headed north with Gord and some colleagues along the Terminal Range. We drove in the pale twilight that even now, at July's end, would last until sunrise only three hours away. Then the range tapered off to a bald, unnamed dome bulging out of a green cowl of spruce.

"The last mountain," said Gord. "The end of the Rockies."

Beyond stretched the Liard Plateau, its forest razed by fire. The humpbacked hills were magenta with fireweed, the first plant to come back, and through it gray spars bristled like quills on a porcupine. From the rises you could see hills rolling north in a smokelike haze out of which looped the broad brown surge of the Liard River.

"The Liard was one of the routes to the Yukon gold rush," Gord said. "About 12 miles down it narrows to a gorge and spurts through like a fire hose. So many prospectors were lost they named it the 'Rapids of the Drowned.'"

At Mile 498 we parked beside a swamp. A rank growth of birch, spruce, and fern enclosed a steaming pool: the field party's weekly bathtub. "There are hot springs all through this area," Gord said. "Waterfalls. Fantastic hoodoos. The only people who see them are geologists and bush pilots."

I had my last look at the Rockies in the patched-up helicopter, swaying as in a Ferris wheel while mountains slid beneath us. We followed the Gataga River, running like spilled chocolate milk through mud flats. Gord made charts as we flew.

The timber retreated. The meadows thinned. Snow whitened the gullies and ridges, and above them reared the cloud-surfed peaks like reefs in a frozen sea. High on a slope four Stone sheep turned toward us the black heads prized by hunters; we were more than 200 miles beyond the northernmost range of the bighorn.

We landed on a snow-covered ridge to gas up from a fuel cache. Glaciers uncoiled from clefts on every side. There was no pattern to the ranges, no human association. It was prehistoric chaos, as raw as a world in crucible.

The ridge was shale with a few small clumps of yellow lichen, that strange internal partnership of an alga and a fungus, eroding the rock with its acids a millimeter a century, creating soil for a new succession of plant life.

A piece of shale cracked off and fell, lost forever to the mountain. In a few eons, gravity, lichen, frost, wind, and rain would level one of the highest, hardest masses in the world. The sense of mystery was strong: the mystery of this rock, a substance from the very depths of the earth pushed skyward to sink again, like ocean waves in infinitely slow motion.

This is not yet tourist country. But someday, I reflected, as the plane swung me up on the first leg of my trip home, it will be. Someday when the bulk of the continent is overlain with asphalt this will be a refuge where people can refresh their frazzled nerves, and lose themselves in the wonder of it all.

In the silent, desolate grandeur of these northernmost Rockies, the most arrogant mind must experience humility. The towering peaks confront us with the ancient mystery of creation, the dual challenge of adventure and discovery: what lies beyond, beyond the next mountain range, beyond the known?

Past Emperor Falls a guide tugs his mount and pack horse. The trail skirts 12,972-foot Mount Robson, highest peak of Canada's Rockies. Author Alan Phillips dismounts for a drink in the northern Sentinel Range. An Ontarian, he has written for magazines, movies, radio, and TV. In his book, The Living Legend, *he tells the story of the Royal Canadian Mounted Police.*

YUKON

In the footsteps of the gold seekers to a land of treasure and tragedy— and the promise of new bonanzas

BY W. E. GARRETT
National Geographic Staff

WITHIN MOMENTS after the steamer *Portland* docked at Seattle in July, 1897, the cry raced through the streets: "Gold! Gold by the ton! Gold found in the Klondike!"

With each telling, the ton of yellow metal carried on the *Portland* from Canada's desolate Yukon Territory grew, and seemingly you had only to journey north to the distant town of Dawson to pick up a fortune in nuggets from the creek beds.

Caught up in the excitement of discovery and by the vision of quick, easy riches, at least 100,000 men — and a number of women — set out for the Yukon. Many of them went by way of Alaska to cross the Chilkoot and White Passes, remote, arduous gateways into Canada through the Coast Mountains. During the winter of 1897-98, gold fever drove more than 20,000 of these "stampeders" to challenge the 35-mile Chilkoot.

Once across the mountain barrier, they built boats and paddled 550 miles down the Yukon River to Dawson and the nearby Klondike gold fields. Their incredible adventures and tragic deaths cursed the stampede with an infamy which still conjures

Lust for gold drives prospectors of 1898 up the Alaska side of the Chilkoot Trail. Relaying a ton of supplies per man, they faced storm and avalanche to reach Canada's Yukon Territory.

COURTESY WALLACE W. ATWOOD

177

legends of lonely, disappointed men and their faithful Malemutes in an endless land of paralyzing cold.

Seven decades later, my family and I visited Skagway, Alaska. There, and at neighboring Dyea, the gold seekers had begun their trek to the Yukon. In just one year Skagway had burgeoned from a single settler's cabin into the biggest, toughest town in Alaska. A transient population of some 15,000 included opportunists who fed, housed, entertained, supplied, robbed

THE AUTHOR: NATIONAL GEOGRAPHIC *Senior Assistant Editor W. E. Garrett has won national recognition for his writing and photography. He co-produced and narrated the Society television feature* Alaska! *and received a citation from the Alaska legislature for his work.*

—and even murdered—the prospectors.

Today only 750 people live there. I arrived with my wife Lucille and our sons Mike and Kenny on the modern Alaska ferry system, which regularly takes visitors to the ghostlike town via the Inside Passage.

Except for the decline in population, Skagway remains much the way the gold rush left it. Boardwalks and old saloons line the dusty main street. At the Trail of '98 Museum we met receptionist Jeannette Hillery, a resident of the town for 68 of its 70 years. We told her that the poems of Robert Service and the tales of Jack London and Rex Beach had inspired us to try to climb the Chilkoot ourselves. Mrs. Hillery, who had followed the trail part way in her youth, explained its man-killer reputation in the

At Canada's rocky doorstep, author W. E. Garrett and his family breakfast on the Alaska-British Columbia border high above Crater Lake. Standing atop a cache of boat kits abandoned at the summit by an entrepreneur of '98, Kenny shows a moldering bundle to his brother Mike. The prospectors, after crossing the Chilkoot, assembled crude boats to navigate 550 miles down the Yukon River to the Klondike gold creeks.

W. E. GARRETT, NATIONAL GEOGRAPHIC STAFF

gentle tones of a teacher who knows and loves her subject.

"It's not as bad as the old stories make it. You have to realize that the men who suffered so on the Chilkoot were soft. They were 'cheechakos,' as we call them. Many, like my father, had been clerical workers. For some the trail was more than they could stand. In the spring of 1898 I saw wagons go by our home carrying loads of men with strange expressions on their faces. They had gone mad, my mother told me, all alone in the Yukon winter. After that the Mounties insisted that the men take a partner or a dog or cat — someone or something they could talk to."

My family and I didn't plan to stay but we did take along Brandy, our St. Bernard.

For the first few hours we walked along a well-marked path through dense forest. By evening the trail steepened — and the mosquitoes seemed hungrier. We stayed the first night in one of the two new cabins built by the State of Alaska to shelter hikers.

The next day we climbed a treacherous slope of loose, sliding rock. For 13 hours we labored upward, finally reaching the desolate summit line of the Coast Mountains,

WHITE HORSE

the border between Alaska and Canada.

The lawlessness that characterized Skagway in 1898 ceased abruptly here. North-West Mounted Police met every gold seeker and checked to see that he relayed the ton of supplies a man needed to survive in the Yukon for one year. Despite the 70 feet of snow that fell on the pass in 1898, the Mounties stayed on. Down by Bennett Lake they kept an eye on boat construction. "Build strong," they cautioned. "Don't start for Dawson in a floating coffin."

But now the Mounties were gone from the pass. As we stood exhausted on the mountaintop that evening, we shivered in the same chill wind which met the thousands pouring past this spot in their stampede for the Yukon gold. An inhospitable rock ledge bordering the snowcap became our bivouac for the night.

Lucille feared the boys might walk in their sleep and fall off the ledge. From his sleeping bag Mike reassured her, "I'm not walking *anywhere* tonight."

As we rested our aching muscles, we thought of the many women who had preceded Lucille to this spot. Any who reached the Yukon towns in 1898 could get married or rich or both. Some found these prospects irresistible. One, impatient to move on, ignored avalanche warnings following a blizzard and was caught in a snowslide which killed her and some 60 other victims.

For four days we walked over the bones

AMOS BURG (ABOVE) AND MELVILLE BELL GROSVENOR, NATIONAL GEOGRAPHIC STAFF

Relic of the gold rush, one of the last stern-wheelers still operating on the Yukon River in 1953 stops at Whitehorse, capital of the Yukon Territory. Others sit high and dry, remnants of the great fleet of 250 steamers that carried prospectors, gamblers, and adventurers to the Klondike. Today, none of the vessels remain in use; hulls rot on sandbars. Outside the Yukon Historical Museum in Whitehorse, Frank Melvin, of the U. S. National Park Service, and Mrs. Melville Bell Grosvenor examine a 2,590-pound nugget of copper, a mineral that promises new bonanzas. Already, mining interests have invested millions of dollars to begin open-pit production near Whitehorse in the territory's "Copper Belt."

End of the Yukon trail: At its zenith, now-quiet Dawson thronged with thousands of gold seekers. One who stampeded to the Klondike, Pat Brady (left) still panned the surrounding creeks at the age of 93. Can-can girls at Skagway, Alaska, evoke the past in the frolic "Days of '98!"

of the gold rush, sleeping in the only cabin left in long-deserted Lindeman on the Canadian side of the Chilkoot. In the ruins of a blacksmith shop we discovered sledge runners, wagon wheels, and hundreds of horse and mule shoes.

Cached in a crevice 4,000 feet above sea level lay some 100 wood and canvas boat kits, untouched for 70 years. At the end of the trail of '98 they would have fetched a fancy price from prospectors desperate to push on to Dawson and the

creeks with the siren names: Bonanza, Eldorado, Gold Bottom. What happened to the entrepreneur who had brought them so far? No one knows. Perhaps he was one of the cheechakos for whom the trail had been too much.

His failure was typical of that of the dreamers who suffered and struggled.

Well before that long line of bent men took the first step on the Chilkoot, the gold fields in the northland had been staked by men already there when George Carmack

W. E. GARRETT, NATIONAL GEOGRAPHIC STAFF (BELOW) AND NATIONAL GEOGRAPHIC PHOTOGRAPHER DAVID S. BOYER

made his Bonanza Creek discovery on August 17, 1896. Thousands of men survived almost unbelievable hardships to reach Dawson, but few found the fortune they sought. Though most pushed on to the creeks with picks and mining pans, many simply wandered the muddy streets in bewilderment, asking, "Where do we dig?"

BUT THE STRIKE blew the lid off Dawson. At the peak of the gold rush, every third door opened into a saloon. A man paid for his whiskey by throwing his poke on the bar. The bartender weighed out the price of a drink and tossed back the poke. A careful barkeep kept a cloth under the scales to collect for himself any spilled dust. Some, it is said, coated their whiskers with molasses to pick up the precious yellow flakes from the bar.

The Flora Dora Dance Hall promised the miners entertainment—and cleaned them out of their fortunes. A patron gladly paid a dollar a minute for a turn around the floor with the girl of his choice. There Nellie the Pig, in an angry moment, bit off a bartender's ear. Gertie Lovejoy, who had a diamond fastened between her two front teeth, danced as Diamond-Tooth Gertie, and diminutive Cad Wilson strutted about, listing from the weight of a $50,000 belt of nuggets given her by smitten miners.

On our final day of tramping over land the gold seekers knew, dense underbrush slowed us as we hiked toward a narrow-gauge railroad connecting Skagway and Whitehorse, capital of the Yukon Territory. Only by running the last hundred yards did we reach the tracks in time to flag the train that would take us back to Skagway by way of White Pass, Chilkoot's old rival as a gateway to the Yukon.

Canada's northernmost railroad, the White Pass and Yukon Route was rushed to completion in two years by a determined Irishman named Michael Heney, who hired disillusioned prospectors, including doctors, lawyers, bankers, teachers, and bookkeepers. The 110-mile line, still the only land road out of Skagway, climbs one of the steepest railroad grades in the world, much

of it blasted out of solid rock. The completion of the first 40 miles of track in 1899 signaled the end of the Chilkoot and White Pass Trails, and opened a new and better door to Canada.

By 1905, electric dredges had virtually taken over the gold fields. These huge machines, moving slowly across the land, wrenched more than $200,000,000 in gold from the Yukon in the 70 years following the stampede.

At the end of 1966, gold production had fallen below $2,000,000 annually and the dredges had ceased operation. Nevertheless, some of the fever of '98 lingers on. But virtually no one thinks in terms of gold these days. Now the territory looks optimistically to a new era of major exploration and development of its resources of copper, asbestos fiber, lead, zinc, and silver as more and more mining companies tap new bonanzas.

The White Pass and Yukon Route hauls increasing tonnages of these minerals, but passengers, we found, still ride in quaint old coaches heated by coal stoves. Their automobiles may accompany them by flatcar to the highway at Whitehorse.

This modern city of 4,700 plays host to more than 20 times that number of travelers annually as their cars roll up the Alaska Highway. Many take side trips to the Klondike, visiting in comfort the now-silent gold creeks. Ironically, these present-day cheechakos, with their welcome tourist dollars, are gradually returning the wealth that flowed from the territory after the stampede of '98.

Narrow-gauge railway shuttles freight and passengers through White Pass, where gold-hungry men trudged on their way to Canada. Before the railroad came, this corridor offered stampeders an alternate to the shorter, but much steeper, Chilkoot Trail. Pushed through the gap in a matter of months with the labor of disheartened prospectors, the White Pass and Yukon Route made its first run in 1899, ending forever the agonizing trek across the mountains. Today the 110-mile line links Skagway and Whitehorse.

VANCOUVER VICTORIA

Gateways to the Pacific world:
harbors with many islands—
and pleasant echoes of England

BY BERRY REECE

AN OFFSHORE BREEZE, scented by ever-greens, tingled our faces as the 36-foot power cruiser *Valére* roared along Vancouver's English Bay. Off the port bow rose a colonnade of skyscrapers. Astern loomed sapphire mountains, some tipped with snow, a few streaked with ski lifts.

Here, where the Coast Mountains march toward the Inside Passage with its many islands, lies the chief metropolis of British Columbia—bonny and shiny and alive.

Our host, Norm Yelland, cut the engines, and we bobbed adrift in the warm June sun. From the galley he passed out a tray heaped with ham and cheese sandwiches. My wife Mary Jo and I and our daughters, Georganne and Mara, then 7 and 2, attacked them like famished mariners.

Norm, a Vancouver businessman and

Towering skyscrapers and wooded Stanley Park crowd an arm of land at Vancouver, below the Coast Mountains. Deep channels reach from this booming British Columbia port to the Pacific.

JOE MUNROE

Penguins strut at Stanley Park, a thousand acres of forest and fun. At the annual Caledonian Games there, a contestant dances the sailor's hornpipe, a bandsman pounds his drum, and pipers skirl a quickstep. Flags held high, a color guard marches during the Obon Festival, when Japanese welcome the spirits of their ancestors. Cricketers defend wickets on summer afternoons, and ladies meet for lawn bowling. A doorman dressed as a Beefeater welcomes guests to Bayshore Inn, not far from the park.

KING PENGUINS AND A HUMBOLDT PENGUIN CAVORT BESIDE A MOAT.

Vice-Commodore of the Burrard Yacht Club, told us, "Downtown you're surrounded by buildings and people. Out here you can lose yourself—alone with the sea and the mountains and your thoughts."

As I gazed at the tall buildings ashore, I tried to visualize what Capt. George Vancouver of the Royal Navy had seen when he explored English Bay in 1792 during his search for the Northwest Passage. In the pinnace and launch of H.M.S. *Discovery*, he and Lt. Peter Puget scanned a panorama changeless and silent, except for the creak of the boats, the mewing of gulls. Peaks. Deep forests. Waters of the Pacific easing around the tip of Vancouver Island, a 285-mile-long mountain-spined breakwater.

However keen his eye for a good anchorage, Captain Vancouver could hardly have foreseen today's great, clanging port of roughly a million people, third largest city in Canada. It has become an outdoorsman's paradise where 40,000 pleasure craft nestle in a labyrinthine harbor with a shoreline a hundred miles long.

Vancouver was the first European to chart Burrard Inlet, today the inner harbor. Three leagues or so up the inlet, the British sailors spent a distressing night on the north shore. Some tried sleeping in the two small boats. Others, as Vancouver wrote,

BAND PLAYS FOR THE 1966 CALEDONIAN GAMES.
QUEEN'S KEYS MARK BEEFEATER COSTUME.

THE AUTHOR: *Berry Reece took a transcontinental tour of Canada with his wife and two daughters—and found the west coast especially captivating. He was a member of the Society's staff from 1964 to 1968 and is now a senior editor at Houghton Mifflin Company in Boston.*

JOE MUNROE

ANGUS MACKENZIE, NO. 152, TRIES FOR A TROPHY.

YOUNG NISEI CELEBRATE DURING A SUMMER FESTIVAL.

BATSMAN DRIVES THE BALL PAST THE WICKET KEEPER.
CLOTH STRIPS KEEP GRASS STAINS OFF BOWLERS' KNEES.

PIPERS COMPETE IN SCOTTISH MARCHES.

JOE MUNROE

Skyride climbs Grouse Mountain, rising 2,624 feet in less than five minutes. Far below, Lions Gate Bridge arches a narrows of Burrard Inlet to Stanley Park. Beyond downtown Vancouver lies the Strait of Georgia. Capilano Suspension Bridge spans a gorge 230 feet deep.

"preferring the stony beach for their couch, without duly considering the line of high water mark, found themselves incommoded by the flood tide, of which they were not apprized until they were nearly afloat."

Our lunch finished, we plowed off in Vancouver's wake, making for the Lions Gate Bridge, which crosses the inlet's First Narrows. The bridge takes its name from The Lions, twin peaks on the north shore said to resemble the heraldic British lions. At the helm Norm relished the spray pelting his face. "This is where I love to be," he said. "When I'm cruising home with my family from a weekend and the weather's a little wet, I stand up here in the rain, looking out for driftwood."

He gestured with his pipe toward a half-submerged log as we turned into the inlet. Here pass the huge log booms headed for the whining blades of the sawmills. Lumbering in this area dates from the 1840's, when a Hudson's Bay Company mill shipped its first cargo of timber to the San Francisco market. Now, lumber is king in these parts.

Norm dropped us off on the pier, literally at the back door of our hotel, the Bayshore Inn. Businessmen often arrive in floatplanes to dine here at Trader Vic's. It's a far cry from one of the inlet's first hostelries, owned by "Gassy Jack" Deighton, a voluble old salt who commenced operations with two hens, one yellow dog, one Indian wife, and one barrel of whiskey.

When we arrived, Vancouver was celebrating its annual Sea Festival, with parades, fireworks, regattas, water ski shows, and concerts in the modern Queen Elizabeth Theatre. For me, the most notable event was the race of Indian war canoes. I watched from the deck of a tubby black fisherman anchored in the bay to serve as start, finish, press box, and judges' stand. Scampering cameramen jostled old Indian chiefs in mufti, here to see their favorite teams in action.

Stretching from the stern, the starting line bobbed on corks. At intervals along it, nine arrowlike war canoes, each with a crew of eleven, lay poised on the water.

"Get ready for the whistle!" yelled the starter. "All you crew captains hang on to the cork line!"

Black-haired, copper-skinned crewmen —sawmill, cannery, factory workers—lifted their paddles. The whistle blew.

"Hey! Hey! Hey!" barked the paddlers as they began chopping the water at 40 strokes a minute. The canoes bolted toward that towering skyline, perhaps a mile away.

On the second lap, *Mt. Prevost*, the favorite, led. But in the turn, she veered too close to our ship's anchor cable. With a sickening crack, her prow splintered. Her crew struggled wildly to stay upright, floundering out of the race. *Squamish Chieftan* surged ahead.

"Come on, *Chieftan!*" growled a voice at my elbow. Chief Frank Miranda—a spry septuagenarian who had brooded over his young North Vancouver tribesmen during the long spring season of canoe races—

flagged them on with his gray fedora. It had been 33 years since he had raced. But he still remembered how it felt.

Sinews glistened. Strokes slowed down—perhaps to 15 a minute. Coxswains yelled more frequently for a switch; then left and right paddlers alike would gasp *One! Two!* and shift to the opposite side.

On the last lap, *Squamish Chieftan* ran away with it. Miranda waved his hat with a "Hyahh!" The championship of the year!

"From February till now," said the old man with a wide grin, "is a long time to keep training." But tonight? Tonight, there would be a great festival.

To celebrate major events, North Pacific Indians traditionally held a potlatch, an elaborate feast at which the host practiced one-upmanship by strewing a showy wealth of gifts among his guests. After the race, we attended a sort of nightly potlatch at "Captain" Harry Almas's The Ship of the Seven Seas, an old North Vancouver ferry converted into a charming moored restaurant. Our host's specialty, a smorgasbord of 54 varieties of seafood, established him as quite a tolerable one-upper.

We piled our plates with smoked Alaska cod, Dungeness crab, shrimp, herring and halibut and salmon, trout and oysters and sturgeon. We even sampled an octopus, cooked to a pink and augustly splayed at the head of the table—chewy, but good.

Great quantities of such treasures from the sea arrive at Vancouver from June until October in the icy holds of fishing vessels, trawlers, seiners, and whalers.

One of the great Pacific Coast salmon fleets operates out of New Westminster, an industrial suburb near the Fraser River mouth. Hereabouts, in 1808, Simon Fraser,

stocky, Scottish-Canadian *bourgeois,* or partner in the North West Company, probed with his little band of buckskinned fur traders. Within sight of the Strait of Georgia, they retreated from a hostile Indian band, abruptly concluding their westerly exploration of that powerful stream.

Along the Trans-Canada Highway you can follow the river 210 miles east to the salmon ladders at Hells Gate, scene of one of Fraser's most hair-raising adventures. Trying to run that thundering maelstrom would have meant certain death. So the voyagers cached their canoes and followed their guides over Indian paths and wobbly branch-and-vine ladders hundreds of feet up the sheer walls of the canyon. "We had to pass where no human beings should venture," wrote Fraser. During this trek, the footing was "so small as to render it, at times, difficult even for one person sideways."

One hundred fifty years after Fraser, the Trans-Canada and two main railways, the Canadian Pacific and the Canadian National, share this narrow corridor. Along their routes, blasted out of the cliffsides, Indians still have paths to the canyon and platforms for drying their salmon. A few villages, built for railway workers, nestle on the slopes. They are sheltered from above by firs and cedars seeded from the vast trees, 15 feet in diameter, of Fraser's day.

We followed the Trans-Canada from

Hotels and apartment houses rim Vancouver's English Bay Beach. Office workers from the city's nearby commercial district often stroll its sands at noon. Sunbathers at right rest among logs that broke free from floating booms and washed ashore. A major business since the 1840's, lumbering today ranks as the Vancouver area's top industry.

Clear summer sky affords a sweeping vista of Vancouver's skyline to tourists crossing English Bay in a canopied power cruiser. To many Vancouverites, boats are a way of life—yachtsmen can sail in the shadows of buildings or explore the islands and inlets of the Strait of Georgia. A girl (left) watches her brother gather starfish near a Vancouver wharf.

Indians lean to the paddles, knifing water 40 times a minute in a race across English Bay during Vancouver's annual Sea Festival. Hewn from cedar logs and polished glass-smooth, such narrow dugouts sometimes exceed 50 feet in length. Long ago Pacific Coast tribes used similar craft in warring over fishing and hunting grounds.

JOE MUNROE (BELOW) AND TOBY RANKIN, CANADA WIDE FEATURE SERVICE, LIMITED

Vancouver northeast to dude-ranch country. At Ashcroft, where the Thompson River surges through hills daubed with tumbleweed and sagebrush, we spent a couple of carefree days at the Bar Q.

In the stable were 63 splendid horses, and from the time we left the air-conditioned ranch house early each morning until we entered the lounge at sundown, we rode, rode, rode. Loping across those high meadows, ambling along those ridges of jack pine and Douglas fir, with shifting vistas of mauve mountains, would please any dude.

On one ride, we met Rudy Stanford, a Vancouver toy importer, world traveler, and an excellent equestrian. In his native Vienna he had learned to ride from a trainer of the famed Lipizzan breed. Rudy fled Austria in 1938 after Hitler annexed the country. One afternoon as he and I paddled about the ranch pool and basked in the sun, with music flowing from a nearby speaker as smoothly as a Strauss waltz, he smiled thoughtfully and said, "Life can be beautiful." And I fancied that it may not always have been so for this warm and gentle man.

Ashcroft stands at the gateway of the storied Cariboo region—land of the big sky, of the big cattle ranch. The gold rush of the 1860's to that northern area of British Columbia made the Cariboo Road a tumultuous thoroughfare. Of the tens of thousands of stampeders who poured up that trail, many were Chinese. In the 1880's another wave of them arrived, imported as cheap, sober, long-suffering labor to help the Irish lay the B.C. portion of the Canadian Pacific Railway. "It was built by tea drinkers and whiskey drinkers," said Roy Mah, editor of Vancouver's *Chinatown News,* an English-language magazine.

We had met for tea at the golden-tapestried Lotus Gardens restaurant in Vancouver. Though the city's Chinatown ranks as one of the largest in North America, its ways have changed. Opium dens no longer fume. The tongs, originally family protection guilds, no longer war with one another. Tong halls, Roy declared, now serve as meeting places for social fraternities. Res-

idents visit the halls to read Chinese periodicals or to enjoy a game of mah jong— "our version of rummy, played with tiles." Many second-generation Chinese Canadians work in Vancouver as doctors, lawyers, and dentists, and live in the suburbs.

Yet the old flavor of Chinatown remains. Pender Street in the summer's inescapable rain offered a steaming exotic vignette. Here and there goateed old men huddled in doorways, puffing pipes and muttering Cantonese. The windows of gilded and carved shop-fronts displayed jade and ivory, teak and rattan, silk and brocade. The capricious pungency of fish, pork, jasmine, and ginger lay on the air.

But nowhere were the aromas of the Orient more tantalizing than at the Lotus Gardens. That evening Mary Jo and I dined on Cantonese chow mein, snow peas, a delightful delicacy called "Wandering Dragon," and an exquisite lemon chicken.

THE NEXT DAY WAS SUNNY, a reminder that Vancouver weather is remarkably mild—roses sometimes bloom at Christmas. We went for an outing in Stanley Park. Five minutes from the heart of town, this forested thousand-acre promontory may lure as many as 20,000 Vancouverites on a holiday.

Near Brockton Point perches the nine o'clock gun, a vintage muzzle-loader fired electronically each evening so punctually that inhabitants—some as distant as 40 miles—traditionally set their watches by it. Not far away lies a popular cluster: the Zoo, the Children's Zoo, a miniature railway, and the Aquarium, Canada's finest.

In the waning afternoon we drove across the Lions Gate Bridge and headed for Grouse Mountain, one of the peaks with ski facilities a half-hour from the city center. On a huge aerial lift we whirred and swayed 2,600 feet to a chalet on the summit.

As the setting sun washed the clouds a vivid rose, the fertile farmlands of the Fraser valley darkened away to the south, and the ridges of Vancouver Island were silhouetted across the Strait of Georgia to the west. At the foot of Grouse Mountain,

Sightseers ride a tallyho near Victoria's Empress Hotel. Puppets spar before a summer audience at Butchart Gardens, and a diver performs with an octopus during a show at the Undersea Gardens.

the Upper Levels Highway snaked its way northwest toward Howe Sound. Below us lights began winking and Vancouver sparkled like a tray of diamonds.

Tomorrow when the sun stripped her of mist, the light would reveal a young city, still a bit ingenuous, robust with traces of the frontier and the vigor of new Canadians. But the night was made for farewells. And so we bade ours.

Clouds of silver and lead puffed across the sky as our ferry, *Queen of Saanich,* cut the placid blue waters of the Strait of Georgia toward Victoria. Seagulls hovered above the starboard wing of the bridge.

"We cruise at 16 knots," said Capt. Lloyd Jones, lowering his binoculars. "That's rather good for a 3,500-ton ship. She can carry 106 cars—or 150 Volkswagens."

Numerous cruise ships and freighters ply the Inside Passage. A rakish ferry, *Queen of Prince Rupert,* with berths and staterooms and dining rooms, makes a 20-hour run from Kelsey Bay to Prince Rupert. There it connects with the Alaska ferry system, a new ship-and-highway route that cuts 800 miles of driving from a trip between Seattle and Fairbanks.

Now we headed southwest through the Gulf Islands. Along with enormous Vancouver Island, they comprise the southwesterly paroxysm of the Coast Mountains before they plunge into the depths of the Pacific. Here, strung together by ferry, water taxi, and sailboat, lie a thousand safe bays, some teeming with salmon, some known only to beach parties, clam-diggers, and oyster-hunters. We twisted past one rocky, forested mass after another.

As we steamed into port at Swartz Bay on Vancouver Island, the ship's horn blasted three dots and a dash—"V"—for Victoria. We scrambled below to our car and started up the ramp.

We drove south along the Saanich Peninsula, past strawberry and loganberry and holly farms. The serpentine Marine Drive, with scalloped panoramas of the Strait of

Afternoon tea at the Empress Hotel—with hot crumpets—provides a bit of England for guests in the lobby. Not far away a bronze Queen Victoria surveys her namesake city. Behind her rise the

Parliament Buildings, seat since 1898 of British Columbia's government. Bunting of red and blue commemorates the union in 1866 of the colonies of Vancouver Island and British Columbia.

Thousands of lights trace the domed Parliament Buildings, mirrored in placid Inner Harbour. First set aglow in 1897 to celebrate Queen Victoria's Diamond Jubilee, the façade's bright border now shines daily from dusk to midnight. In downtown Victoria, baskets of flowers hang from lampposts. Double-decker buses, like those of London, await passengers on Government Street, where shops offer English woolens and tweeds, Scottish tartans, Irish lace, and a variety of Indian handicrafts.

Mimicking totem figures, vacationers linger in Thunderbird Park amid one of the world's finest displays of the Indian carvings.

Juan de Fuca, offers a charming introduction to the city.

In Beacon Hill Park, we skirted cricket pitch, bowling green, and ponds where swans and ducks swam among lily pads. Then suddenly we were in the city. Along the Causeway, red double-decker buses were parked beneath lampposts hung with flower pots. In the Inner Harbour, a ship discharged passengers practically at the doors of two venerable turn-of-the-century edifices: the domed Parliament Buildings and the ivy-cowled Empress Hotel.

If Vancouver is the younger and more vigorous sister, Victoria is the smaller and more reserved.

Sunnier, too. Victoria receives only 27 inches of annual rainfall, half that of Vancouver. The California Current blesses the island with a lushness hardly rivaled in Canada. At the Butchart Gardens, floral showcase of the region, 25 acres of color explode in a onetime limestone quarry. In the spring, forget-me-nots, azaleas, daffodils, tulips, and the renowned blue poppy of Tibet flourish by waterfalls, pools, and carpetlike lawns.

Though she wears it well, Victoria *has* a past. A few blocks up Government Street lies the site where James Douglas and his settlers in 1843 constructed Fort Victoria, with 18-foot-high palisades, and guarded it with nine-pounders and muskets.

Later, Victoria became a springboard to the Cariboo, and miners returned to the capital of the colony to sell a little gold and go on a spree. An early item in the *Victoria Gazette* reported, "There has not been a death from natural causes in the city during the last thirty days." And an editorial complained, "Coroner's inquests have to be held in the open air in front of the jail, the jury standing around the corpse, the latter spread on boards . . . whilst the Coroner sits on an empty barrel."

Lured by low-priced land, Englishmen settled Victoria, their queen's namesake. The Royal Navy founded the strategic base at nearby Esquimalt. In time, the capital became a retirement haven for British colonels. Land values are much higher now; the military pensions don't buy what they used to; and Victoria has lost much of her old image. Plus fours and the walrus moustache no longer symbolize the city. Yet dowagers still give garden parties, downtown shops display china and woolens "from home," and many citizens say Victoria is so English "it brings tea to your eyes."

At the Empress Hotel we found that the nostalgia of empire days lingers like the scent of lavender. Paintings of the charge of the Light Brigade hang on corridor walls. And 50 dozen crumpets a day during the summer season are prepared for tea served in a spacious lounge.

Mary Jo and I shared some anxiety about whether little Mara could contain her rather free-wheeling ways at the Empress tea. We had coached her on the necessity for propriety, but we weren't sure how profoundly we had impressed her. All too soon, we found out. As we reached our table, Mara pointed to a mantelpiece portrait of King George V and cried, "See the funny man," causing our waitress to stiffen a bit.

The following day, I was invited to the Union Club, founded in 1879. This exclusive men's club follows the London tradition as a temple "where women ceased from troubling and the weary were at rest."

Settled in the studded leather captain's chairs of the dark-paneled bar, my host Bill Hawkins and I savored a collection of criticisms that members had placed in the club's Suggestion Book over the years. The pithiest, I think, was entered in 1911: "The Club flag is a disgrace. Ditto the secretary's tie."

We took a tour of the building, culminating at the holy of holies—the Silence Reading Room. Here not a few members in the good old days had been reprimanded for rattling a newspaper.

In ceiling-high bookcases flanking the overstuffed chairs and dark green curtains, stood volumes of another era: *London News, 1891; The Romance of Lincoln's Inn Fields; Burkes Landed Gentry of Ireland, 1900; The Sporting and Dramatic News.*

Then a wild anomaly. In front of the fireplace I saw a TV set. When I looked startled, my host chuckled, "Well—we wouldn't want the thing anywhere else. Certainly not in the bar or the card room." I noticed that the picture was turned on—but the sound was off.

The gilding of this land may be English, but the base is surely Indian. At a lacrosse game one evening at the Memorial Arena, we watched two attack players smash a defenseman into the plywood wall about the hockey-size rink.

"They're going to kill him!" exclaimed Mary Jo, a native Baltimorean, used to the

Tree-shadowed walk curves through flower-splashed Butchart Gardens near Victoria. Once a barren, worked-out limestone quarry, the spot blossomed after its owners began collecting plants from all over the world to mask the ugly scar on their estate. Now, half a century later, some 5,000 varieties flourish here, including the cactus-flowered dahlia (left).

TED SPIEGEL, RAPHO GUILLUMETTE

fast, agile field lacrosse that Chesapeake Bay college students play with such finesse.

"You should have been here last week," chuckled a man behind us. "One fellow was knocked *through* the wall."

This was box lacrosse, or boxla, he explained, with six-man teams thrashing shorter sticks than those of field lacrosse in a smaller, enclosed area. These six-footers played in a rough-and-tumble style that smacked of the original Indian game of baggataway. Yet maybe it was only natural. The white man learned to play lacrosse from the Indians. And in 1867 Canada's Parliament made it the national sport.

Next door to the Empress, in Thunderbird Park, survives North Pacific Indian art at its finest: the resplendent totem poles restored and carved by Mungo Martin. The Kwakiutl chief and master craftsman designed and carved the towering 127-foot totem in Beacon Hill Park and, as a gift to Queen Elizabeth II, a 100-foot pole, the Royal Totem, which now stands in England's Windsor Great Park.

When the old man died in 1962, the Royal Canadian Navy piped his family-carved cedar coffin aboard H.M.C.S. *Ottawa* at Esquimalt. It lay there on the afterdeck, guarded by sentries with fixed bayonets, as the ship headed through the mists of the Inside Passage toward Mungo's final resting place at Alert Bay. It was the first time the Navy had paid such tribute to an Indian.

Perhaps it was high time. After all, the Indians' ancestors reached America thousands of years before any European touched its shores. Almost certainly they crossed from Asia on a vast land bridge that linked the two continents, thus becoming the first to find and settle this vast, beautiful, and incredibly rich New World.

Ferry-liner Queen of Prince Rupert *churns narrow Grenville Channel during her 330-mile run through the Inside Passage. Canadian vessels cruise along the mainland shore of British Columbia and connect with modern year-round Alaskan ferries that thread the islands of the Alexander Archipelago as far north as Skagway.*

INDEX

Illustrations references appear in *italics*.

Composition by National Geographic's Phototypographic Division, John E. McConnell, Manager. Printed and bound by Fawcett Printing Corp., Rockville, Md. Color separations by Beck Engraving Company, Philadelphia, Pa.; Graphic Color Plate, Inc., Stamford, Conn.; The Lanman Engraving Company, Alexandria, Va.; and Progressive Color Corp., Rockville, Md.